Scott Foresman·Addison Wes

enVisionMATH

Illinois

Welcome to Your Grade 3
Overview and Implementation Guide

Authors

Randall I. Charles
Professor Emeritus
Department of Mathematics
San Jose State University
San Jose, California

Janet H. Caldwell
Professor of Mathematics
Rowan University
Glassboro, New Jersey

Mary Cavanagh
Mathematics Consultant
San Diego County Office of Education
San Diego, California

Dinah Chancellor
Mathematics Consultant with Carroll ISD
Southlake, Texas
Mathematics Specialist with Venus ISD
Venus, Texas

Juanita V. Copley
Professor
College of Education
University of Houston
Houston, Texas

Warren D. Crown
Associate Dean for Academic Affairs
Graduate School of Education
Rutgers University
New Brunswick, New Jersey

Francis (Skip) Fennell
Professor of Education
McDaniel College
Westminster, Maryland

Alma B. Ramirez
Sr. Research Associate
Math Pathways and Pitfalls WestEd
Oakland, California

Kay B. Sammons
Coordinator of Elementary Mathematics
Howard County Public Schools
Ellicott City, Maryland

Jane F. Shielack
Professor of Mathematics
Associate Dean for Assessment and
Pre K–12 Education, College of Science
Texas A&M University
College Station, Texas

William Tate
Edward Mallinckrodt Distinguished
University Professor in Arts & Sciences
Washington University
St. Louis, Missouri

John A. Van de Walle
Professor Emeritus, Mathematics Education
Virginia Commonwealth University
Richmond, Virginia

Consulting Mathematicians

Edward J. Barbeau
Professor of Mathematics
University of Toronto
Toronto, Canada

Sybilla Beckmann
Professor of Mathematics
Department of Mathematics
University of Georgia
Athens, Georgia

David Bressoud
DeWitt Wallace Pr...
Macalester College
Saint Paul, Minnes...

Gary Lippman
Professor of Mathe...
California State University East Bay
Hayward, California

Scott Foresman
is an imprint of

PEARSON

Editorial Offices: Glenview, Illinois • Parsippany, New Jersey • New York, New York
Sales Offices: Boston, Massachusetts • Duluth, Georgia • Glenview, Illinois
Coppell, Texas • Sacramento, California • Mesa, Arizona

enVisionMATH is trademarked in the U.S. and/or foreign countries of Pearson Education, Inc. or its affiliate(s)

Consulting Authors

Charles R. Allan
Mathematics Education Consultant
(Retired)
Michigan Department of Education
Lansing, Michigan

Verónica Galván Carlan
Private Consultant Mathematics
Harlingen, Texas

Stuart J. Murphy
Visual Learning Specialist
Boston, Massachusetts

Jeanne Ramos
Secondary Mathematics Coordinator
Los Angeles Unified School District
Los Angeles, California

Center Activities Author

Ruth I. Champagne
Mathematics Education Specialist
FRIENDLY MATH, LLC
Chicago, Illinois

ELL Consultants/ Reviewers

Jim Cummins
Professor
The University of Toronto
Toronto, Canada

Alma B. Ramirez
Sr. Research Associate
Math Pathways and Pitfalls WestEd
Oakland, California

National Math Development Team

Cindy Bumbales
Teacher
Lake in the Hills, IL

Ann Hottovy
Teacher
Hampshire, IL

Deborah Ives
Supervisor of Mathematics
Ridgewood, NJ

Lisa Jasumback
Math Curriculum Supervisor
Farmington, UT

Rebecca Johnson
Teacher
Canonsburg, PA

Jo Lynn Miller
Math Specialist
Salt Lake City, UT

Patricia Morrison
Elementary Mathematics Specialist K–5
Upper Marlboro, MD

Patricia Horrigan Rourke
Mathematics Coordinator
Holliston, MA

Elise Sabaski
Teacher
Gladstone, MO

Math Advisory Board

John F. Campbell
Teacher
Upton, MA

Enrique Franco
Coordinator Elementary Math
Los Angeles, CA

Gladys Garrison
Teacher
Minot AFB, ND

Pat Glubka
Instructional Resource Teacher
Brookfield, UT

Shari Goodman
Math Specialist
Salt Lake City, UT

Cathy Massett
Math Facilitator
Cobb County SD, GA

Mary Modene
Math Facilitator
Belleville, IL

Kimya Moyo
Math Manager
Cincinnati, OH

Denise Redington
Teacher
Chicago, IL

Arlene Rosowski
Supervisor of Mathematics
Buffalo, NY

Darlene Teague
Director of Core Data
Kansas City, MO

Debbie Thompson
Elementary Math Teaching Specialist
Wichita, KS

Michele Whiston
Supervisor Curriculum, Instruction,
and Assessment
Mobile County, AL

ISBN: 978-0-328-33170-3

ISBN: 0-328-33170-8

Copyright © 2009 Pearson Education, Inc.

All Rights Reserved. Printed in the United States of America. This publication is protected by Copyright, and permission should be obtained from the publisher prior to any prohibited reproduction, storage in a retrieval system, or transmission in any form by any means, electronic, mechanical, photocopying, recording, or otherwise. For information regarding permission(s), write to: Permissions Department, Scott Foresman, 1900 East Lake Avenue, Glenview, Illinois 60025.

1 2 3 4 5 6 7 8 9 10 009 16 15 14 13 12 11 10 09 08 07

Many of the designations used by manufacturers and sellers to distinguish their products are claimed as trademarks. Where those designations appear in this book, and Scott Foresman was aware of a trademark claim, the designations have been printed with initial capitals and in cases of multiple usage have also been marked with either ® or ™ where they first appear.

CONTENTS

AUTHORS AND CONTENTS

PROGRAM OVERVIEW

CONTENT OVERVIEW

GLOSSARY

CORRELATIONS

BIBLIOGRAPHY AND INDEX

ABOUT THE AUTHORS

Randall I. Charles
Professor Emeritus,
   Department of Mathematics
San Jose State University
San Jose, California

Randy Charles's writing and research have focused on problem solving. He is a senior author with Pearson Scott Foresman and Pearson Prentice Hall. He was on the writing team for the NCTM Curriculum Focal Points.

Janet H. Caldwell
Professor of Mathematics
Rowan University
Glassboro, New Jersey

Janet Caldwell teaches and directs projects providing professional development to teachers of mathematics. She has received a Professor of the Year Award and a Distinguished Teaching Award.

Mary Cavanagh
Mathematics Consultant
San Diego County Office
   of Education
San Diego, California

Mary Cavanagh works with grades K–6 English language learners and with their families and teachers. Her most recent work includes developing a model math and science curriculum and professional development for after-school programs.

Francis (Skip) Fennell
Professor of Education
McDaniel College
Westminster, Maryland

Skip Fennell's work has focused on number sense and teacher education, as well as policy and mathematics education. He has been president of the National Council of Teachers of Mathematics and a writer of the NCTM Curriculum Focal Points.

Alma B. Ramirez
Senior Research Associate
Math Pathways and Pitfalls
WestEd
Oakland, California

Alma Ramirez is a former elementary school bilingual teacher who now focuses on professional development with a special interest in schools that have high concentrations of English learners.

Kay B. Sammons
Coordinator of Elementary
   Mathematics
Howard County Public Schools
Ellicott City, Maryland

Kay Sammons is responsible for development of curriculum and assessment. She provides professional development for teachers in the areas of curriculum implementation, pedagogy, assessment, and interventions.

Dinah Chancellor

Mathematics Consultant
  with Carroll ISD
Southlake, Texas
Mathematics Specialist
  with Venus ISD, Venus, Texas

Dinah Chancellor serves as a mathematics consultant for a variety of districts throughout Texas. She has a special interest in teaching students to use reasoning and creativity to solve problems.

Juanita V. Copley

Professor, College of Education
University of Houston
Houston, Texas

Nita Copley researches the effectiveness of professional development models for early childhood mathematics teachers and young children's understanding of mathematical concepts, especially word problems and the use of problem-solving strategies.

Warren D. Crown

Associate Dean for
  Academic Affairs
Graduate School of Education
Rutgers University
New Brunswick, New Jersey

Warren Crown has designed educational software for classroom use, and he has worked as an educator of mathematics teachers at Rutgers for the past thirty years.

This program is dedicated to the memory of Dr. John Van de Walle, who passed away shortly before the completion of the program.

Jane F. Schielack

Professor of Mathematics
Associate Dean for Assessment
  and Pre K–12 Education,
  College of Science
Texas A&M University
College Station, Texas

Janie Schielack works with colleagues in a wide variety of fields to help teachers prepare students for possible uses of mathematics in their futures. She was on the writing team for the NCTM Curriculum Focal Points.

William Tate

Edward Mallinckrodt
Distinguished University
  Professor in Arts & Sciences
Washington University
St. Louis, Missouri

Bill Tate is known for his research and development focused on the political and cultural dimensions of mathematics education and urban education. He has been president of the American Educational Research Association.

John A. Van de Walle

Professor Emeritus,
  Mathematics Education
Virginia Commonwealth
  University
Richmond, Virginia

John Van de Walle is well known for his books on mathematics for teachers. Even in retirement, he continued to work in schools on a regular basis, exploring teaching math through problem solving.

GRADE 3 CONTENTS

Illinois Mathematics Performance Descriptors and Illinois Mathematics Assessment Framework Objectives for each Topic are listed throughout these Contents pages.

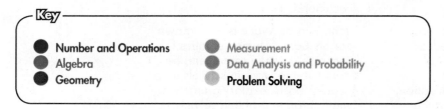

Key

- ● **Number and Operations**
- ● **Algebra**
- ● **Geometry**
- ● Measurement
- ● Data Analysis and Probability
- ● **Problem Solving**

Mathematical Processes, which include problem solving, reasoning, communication, connections, and representations, are infused throughout all lessons.

Topic 3 — Subtraction Number Sense

Performance Descriptors 6C.Stage C.1., 6C.Stage C.2.
Assessment Framework Objectives 6.3.09, 6.3.14, 8.3.03, 8.3.05

Topic 4 — Subtracting Whole Numbers to Solve Problems

Performance Descriptors 6C.Stage C.2., 8A.Stage C.5.
Assessment Framework Objectives 6.3.09, 8.3.03

Topic 5 — Multiplication Meanings and Facts

Performance Descriptors 6B.Stage C.3., 6B.Stage C.5., 8B.Stage C.1., 8B.Stage C.2., 8D.Stage C.1.
Assessment Framework Objectives 6.3.04, 6.3.08, 6.3.13, 8.3.03, 8.3.05

Topic 6 — Multiplication Fact Strategies: Use Known Facts

Performance Descriptors 6B.Stage C.4.
Assessment Framework Objectives 6.3.08, 8.3.05

Topic 11 Congruence and Symmetry

Performance Descriptors 9A.Stage C.3., 9B.Stage C.3.
Assessment Framework Objectives 9.3.04, 9.3.09, 9.3.10

Topic 12 Understanding Fractions

Performance Descriptors 6A.Stage C.3.,
6A.Stage C.4., 8B.Stage C.1.
Assessment Framework Objectives 6.3.03, 8.3.01

Topic 13 Decimals and Money

Performance Descriptors 6A.Stage C.4.,
6A.Stage C.5., 6B.Stage C.7., 8A.Stage C.5.
Assessment Framework Objectives 6.3.03, 6.3.06, 8.3.03,
8.3.05

Topic 14 Customary Measurement

Performance Descriptors 7A.Stage C.2.,
7A.Stage C.3., 7C.Stage C.1., 9B.Stage C.1.
Assessment Framework Objectives 7.3.02, 7.3.05, 7.3.07,
9.3.02

Topic 19 — Dividing with 1-Digit Numbers

Performance Descriptors 6B.Stage C.2., 6B.Stage C.5., 6C.Stage C.1., 6C.Stage C.2.
Assessment Framework Objectives 6.3.01, 6.3.14, 8.3.05

Topic 20 — Data, Graphs, and Probability

Performance Descriptors 10A.Stage C.1., 10A.Stage C.2., 10A.Stage C.3., 10C.Stage C.1., 10C.Stage C.3.
Assessment Framework Objectives 9.3.03, 10.3.01, 10.3.04

Benefits of 20 Topics

- **Focus** Topics are coherent, digestible groups of lessons with a common focus.
- **Flexibility** Topics are small enough to rearrange into a personalized curriculum with your preferred sequence.
- **Convenience** There are 20 Topic Teacher's Editions and 20 Teacher Resource Master pouches. So everything you need to teach lessons in a topic is in just two small items.

Benefits of 140 Lessons

- **Test success this year** You can teach all Grade 3 content before the ISAT test. See Illinois Pacing for Test Success beginning on page T52.
- **Test success next year** You can help prepare students for next year using lessons that preview the next grade and the Math Diagnosis and Intervention System.

PROGRAM OVERVIEW

RESEARCH

A research base to ensure the program "works" for all students

The *en**Vision**MATH* program is based on scientific research on how children learn mathematics as well as on classroom-based evidence that validates proven reliability.

Four distinct phases of research were integrated into the development of the program.

Phase 1
Ongoing Research

Phase 2
Scientific Research Base

Phase 3
Formative Research

Phase 4
Summative Research

Scott Foresman Mathematics, Scott Foresman • Addison Wesley Math, and Silver Burdett Ginn Mathematics programs provide a strong basis for success. Scores on standardized tests as well as longitudinal studies prove these programs help raise math scores.

A randomized control trial conducted on the Scott Foresman • Addison Wesley Math 2005 program by an independent research company showed statistically significant increases in the performance of students using the program.

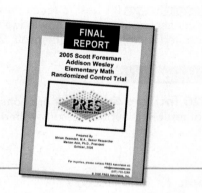

An experienced authorship team incorporated findings from the large body of scientific research available to develop the instructional and assessment tools in *Scott Foresman • Addison Wesley en**Vision**MATH*.

As the program was designed, classroom field studies and leading mathematicians, administrators, teachers, and reviewers contributed valuable input. Pretest and posttest scores proved we were on track.

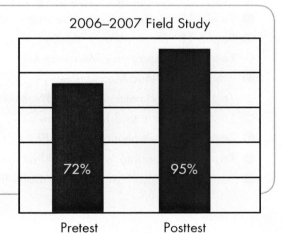

2006–2007 Field Study

Pretest	Posttest
72%	95%

Ongoing scientific research, including longitudinal studies in the classroom, further validates the program's effectiveness and support for our commitment to producing the highest quality mathematics materials.

PERSONALIZED CURRICULUM

Focused

Research says it's best to teach new content by connecting it to prior knowledge with a sustained focus over time (Empson, 2003).

enVisionMATH™ provides:

- **20 focused topics** that are coherent, digestible groups of lessons with a common focus.

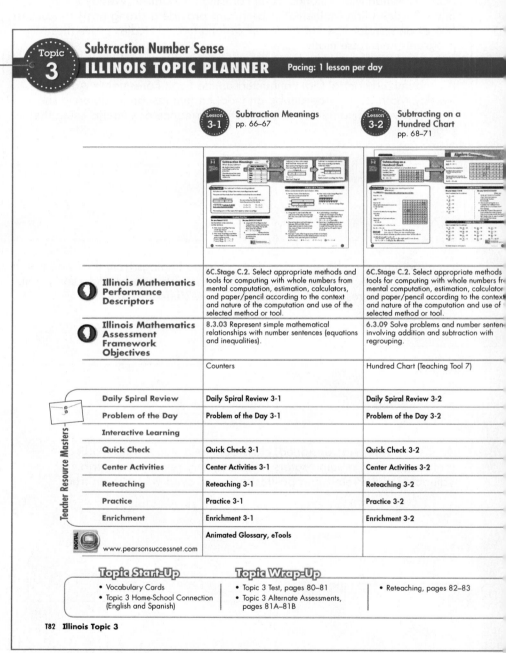

Topic 3 — Subtraction Number Sense

ILLINOIS TOPIC PLANNER   Pacing: 1 lesson per day

Teacher Resource Masters	Lesson 3-1 Subtraction Meanings pp. 66–67	Lesson 3-2 Subtracting on a Hundred Chart pp. 68–71
Illinois Mathematics Performance Descriptors	6C.Stage C.2. Select appropriate methods and tools for computing with whole numbers from mental computation, estimation, calculators, and paper/pencil according to the context and nature of the computation and use of the selected method or tool.	6C.Stage C.2. Select appropriate methods and tools for computing with whole numbers from mental computation, estimation, calculators, and paper/pencil according to the context and nature of the computation and use of the selected method or tool.
Illinois Mathematics Assessment Framework Objectives	8.3.03 Represent simple mathematical relationships with number sentences (equations and inequalities).	6.3.09 Solve problems and number sentences involving addition and subtraction with regrouping.
	Counters	Hundred Chart (Teaching Tool 7)
Daily Spiral Review	Daily Spiral Review 3-1	Daily Spiral Review 3-2
Problem of the Day	Problem of the Day 3-1	Problem of the Day 3-2
Interactive Learning		
Quick Check	Quick Check 3-1	Quick Check 3-2
Center Activities	Center Activities 3-1	Center Activities 3-2
Reteaching	Reteaching 3-1	Reteaching 3-2
Practice	Practice 3-1	Practice 3-2
Enrichment	Enrichment 3-1	Enrichment 3-2
www.pearsonsuccessnet.com	Animated Glossary, eTools	

Topic Start-Up
- Vocabulary Cards
- Topic 3 Home-School Connection (English and Spanish)

Topic Wrap-Up
- Topic 3 Test, pages 80–81
- Topic 3 Alternate Assessments, pages 81A–81B
- Reteaching, pages 82–83

Overview and Implementation Guide

Flexible

Research says that student performance data can influence instructional decisions such as decisions about how to sequence content (Cotton, 2001).

enVisionMATH™ provides:

- **A flexible sequence** with topics that are organized and color coded by content strand and are small enough for you to rearrange into a personalized curriculum that matches the sequence preferred in your class, school, or district.

Paced for

Test Success

Research says that the pace at which new content is presented can be an important factor in how well students learn the content (Shavelson, 1983).

enVisionMATH™ provides:

- **A way to teach all Grade 3 content before the ISAT test** using Illinois Pacing for Test Success beginning on page T52.

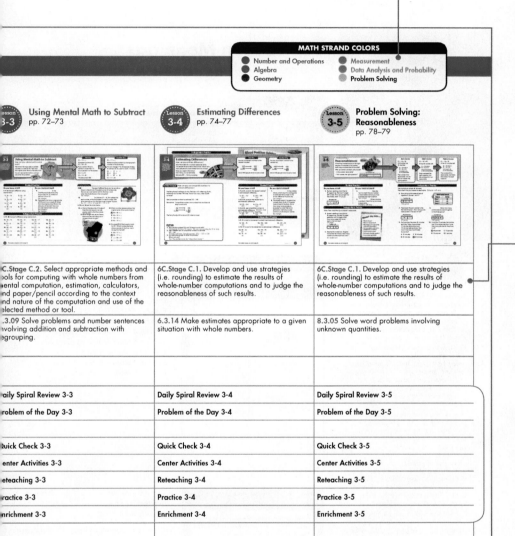

MATH STRAND COLORS

- Number and Operations
- Algebra
- Geometry
- Measurement
- Data Analysis and Probability
- Problem Solving

Lesson 3-3 Using Mental Math to Subtract pp. 72–73	Lesson 3-4 Estimating Differences pp. 74–77	Lesson 3-5 Problem Solving: Reasonableness pp. 78–79
6C.Stage C.2. Select appropriate methods and tools for computing with whole numbers from mental computation, estimation, calculators, and paper/pencil according to the context and nature of the computation and use of the selected method or tool.	6C.Stage C.1. Develop and use strategies (i.e. rounding) to estimate the results of whole-number computations and to judge the reasonableness of such results.	6C.Stage C.1. Develop and use strategies (i.e. rounding) to estimate the results of whole-number computations and to judge the reasonableness of such results.
6.3.09 Solve problems and number sentences involving addition and subtraction with regrouping.	6.3.14 Make estimates appropriate to a given situation with whole numbers.	8.3.05 Solve word problems involving unknown quantities.
Daily Spiral Review 3-3	Daily Spiral Review 3-4	Daily Spiral Review 3-5
Problem of the Day 3-3	Problem of the Day 3-4	Problem of the Day 3-5
Quick Check 3-3	Quick Check 3-4	Quick Check 3-5
Center Activities 3-3	Center Activities 3-4	Center Activities 3-5
Reteaching 3-3	Reteaching 3-4	Reteaching 3-5
Practice 3-3	Practice 3-4	Practice 3-5
Enrichment 3-3	Enrichment 3-4	Enrichment 3-5

Note that digital resources listed in the Topic Planner are the resources referenced in the student textbook. For other digital resources, see pages T38–T39.

Essential Understandings

Research says that teaching for understanding results in better performance that lasts longer (Pesek and Kirshner, 2000).

enVisionMATH™ provides:

- **Essential Understandings** stated explicitly in the Teacher's Edition. The Essential Understandings are connected by Big Ideas. See pages T50–T51.

Daily Spiral Review

Research says that distributed practice (review over time) leads to improved mastery and maintenance (Cotton, 2001).

enVisionMATH™ provides:

- **Daily Spiral Review** masters that focus on foundational skills.

- **Problem of the Day** masters for ongoing practice with a variety of problem types.

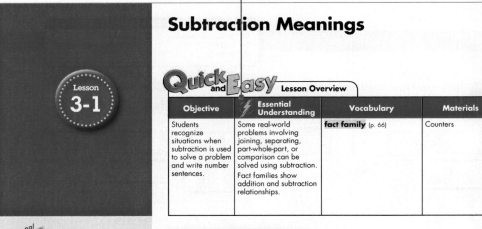

Subtraction Meanings

Lesson 3-1

Quick and Easy Lesson Overview

Objective	Essential Understanding	Vocabulary	Materials
Students recognize situations when subtraction is used to solve a problem and write number sentences.	Some real-world problems involving joining, separating, part-whole-part, or comparison can be solved using subtraction. Fact families show addition and subtraction relationships.	**fact family** (p. 66)	Counters

Math Background for Teachers

Professional Development

Before students can use subtraction effectively in solving problems, they must learn to recognize the types of problem situations that can be modeled by subtraction. This lesson presents three such situations.

The first example at the top of page 73 illustrates *taking away*. In this type of situation, there is an initial amount, an amount is taken away, and there is an amount that is left. This is perhaps the most easily recognizable type of subtraction situation.

The second example illustrates *comparing*. In this type of situation, two amounts are given, as well as the difference between them. These questions often ask how much more, how much less, how much taller, how much shorter, and so on. Sometimes students are given one number and the difference and asked to find the other number: Susie has 5 more books than Joe. Joe has 8 books. How many does Susie have?

Subtraction is also used in *missing addend* situations, as illustrated in Another Example on page 72. When you know two parts, you add to find the whole. Addition and subtraction are inverse operations. That is, one operation "undoes" the other. So, when you know the whole and one of the parts, you subtract to find the missing part.

For more information on subtraction, go to pp. 64A–64B.

66A   Topic 3

1 Daily Spiral Review

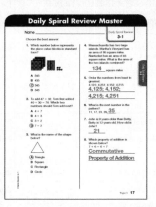

Daily Spiral Review Master

Content Reviewed
- Exercise 1 Write Whole Numbers
- Exercise 2 Model Addition
- Exercise 3 Geometric Shapes
- Exercise 4 Solve Addition Problems
- Exercise 5 Order Whole Numbers
- Exercise 6 Number Patterns
- Exercise 7 Solve Addition Problems
- Exercise 8 Model Addition

Problem of the Day

Problem of the Day   3-1

Find the missing number that completes the fact family.

$$2 + \blacksquare = 8 \qquad 8 - \blacksquare = 2$$
$$\blacksquare + 2 = 8 \qquad 8 - 2 = \blacksquare$$

enVisionMATH

Content Reviewed
Add and Subtract
Use Reasoning

Tip Be sure students understand that the same number goes in the box each time it appears. Have students test their solution to check that it works in four number sentences.

$\blacksquare$ = 6 in all equations

Teacher's Edition Lesson 3-1 from Topic 3: Subtraction Number Sense

Interactive Learning

Interactive Learning • 10–15 min

Overview Students determine the meaning of subtraction and relate addition and subtraction.

Essential Question When do you subtract?

Materials Counters (20 per pair)

....

Engage

Set the Purpose *You know how to add numbers. Today you will use addition to help you to subtract.*

Connect *What are some situations in which you might need to subtract?* [To find out how much money you have left, to compare prices for jeans, etc.] Discuss students' ideas.

....

Pose the Problem *Ling made 14 hats to sell at the fair. She sold 6 of them. How could you draw pictures or use models to find how many hats Ling has now? Work with a partner.* Distribute 20 counters per student pair. Give students time to solve the problem.

Model/ Demonstrate *Which number is the whole?* [14] *How do you know?* [14 is the number of hats Ling starts with.] *Which number is a part of the whole?* [6] *How can you solve the problem?* [Use subtraction. You know one part and the whole. You need to find the other part.] *How can you use addition to help you subtract?* [I can think, 6 plus what number equals 14? I know 6 + 8 = 14, so the missing part is 8. There are 8 hats left.] Have students display and discuss their models or pictures with the class. Lead the discussion to make sure students understand that one method is not better than another.

14 – 6 = 8

Small-Group Interaction Give pairs another subtraction problem such as the following: *Jamie made 18 hats. 7 hats had stripes and the rest had polka dots. How many hats had polka dots? Work with your partner to model the problem. Then write 2 number sentences, one using subtraction and another using addition.* Allow time for students to use counters or diagrams to model the situation. Foster class discussion around using the model to help in developing the number sentences: 18 – 7 = 11; 7 + 11 = 18 or 11 + 7 = 18.

....

Extend

How does addition help you to subtract? Explain your answer to your partner. [Addition and subtraction are related. Addition joins two parts to make the whole. Subtraction starts with the whole and takes away one of the two parts.]

 **eTools** Counters
www.pearsonsuccessnet.com

Link to *Investigations,* **Second Edition**
Joint-Usage Master Plan
Blended Instruction (Plan 1):
Topic 3 and Units 1, 2, 3, and 8

Interactive Learning

Research says that students learn best when they have opportunities to interact with teachers and with other students (Lampert, 1986). It's important for teachers to let students know the purpose of a lesson from the start (Brophy and Good, 1986). Students learn better when new knowledge is connected to prior knowledge in school or in everyday life (Hiebert and Lindquist, 1990). Problem-based instruction (before making math concepts explicit) enhances learning because it gets students actively engaged in thinking about a problem and shows students their thinking is valued (Mack, 1990).

enVisionMATH™ provides:

- **Interactive concept development** where students interact with teachers and other students during a problem-based activity. Interactive Learning (shown here) and Visual Learning (shown on page T18) are two powerful ways to develop conceptual understanding.

The Interactive Learning begins with "Engage" that includes:

- **Set the Purpose** which tells students explicitly what they'll learn that day.
- **Connect** which engages learners by connecting the new lesson to something in the students' prior experiences.

The Interactive Learning continues with:

- **Pose the Problem** which asks students to work on a problem and share their thinking before receiving teacher guidance that makes the math explicit.

The Interactive Learning concludes with:

- **Extend** that provides an additional problem for students to do independently.

Visual Learning

Research says that students benefit from seeing math ideas portrayed pictorially (Schwartz and Heiser, 2006). Effective instruction both focuses on ideas as well as shows connections between ideas (Hiebert and Lindquist, 1990). A good instructional strategy includes teachers asking guiding questions (Carpenter and Fennema, 1992). Pictures are helpful when they provide visual representations of math concepts or illustrate relationships in a problem context (Mayer, 1989).

enVisionMATH™ provides:

- **Visual concept development** that helps students access math skills and concepts by seeing ideas developed in visual displays.

- **Visual Learning Bridge** which is a pictorial, step-by-step bridge between the Interactive Learning activity and the lesson exercises. It helps students focus on one idea at a time as well as see connections within a sequence of ideas. This is especially helpful for visual learners and English language learners.

- **Guiding questions** in blue type that help you guide students through the examples and give you an opportunity to check students' understanding.

- **Pictures with a purpose** throughout the lessons that show representations of math concepts and show data for math problems in real-world contexts.

A **Visual Learning Bridge** is shown at the start of the lesson in the Student Edition and also appears in the Teacher's Edition along with **guiding questions** in blue type.

Visual Learning Animations can be used to present the Visual Learning Bridge digitally with animation. See page T38.

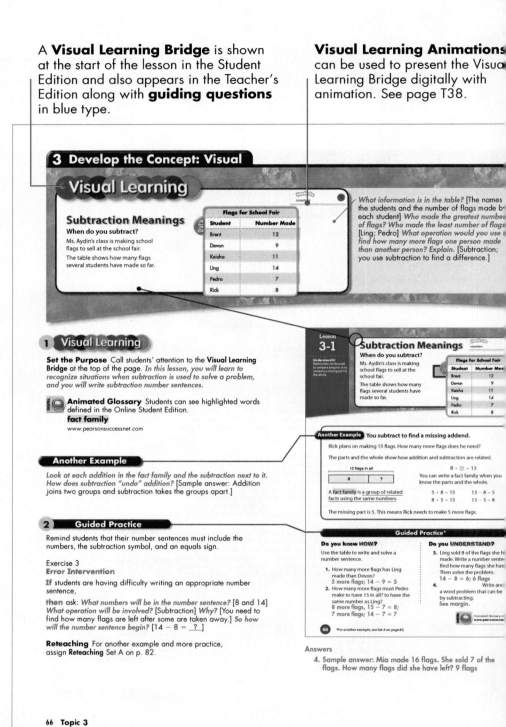

Teacher's Edition Lesson 3-1

Bar diagrams help students solve problems. A bar diagram is a pictorial representation of the quantities in a problem.

For example, if a problem involves parts of a whole (shown as parts of a bar), students see that they can subtract to find an unknown part or add to find an unknown whole. If the parts are equal, students can use multiplication or division to find unknown quantities.

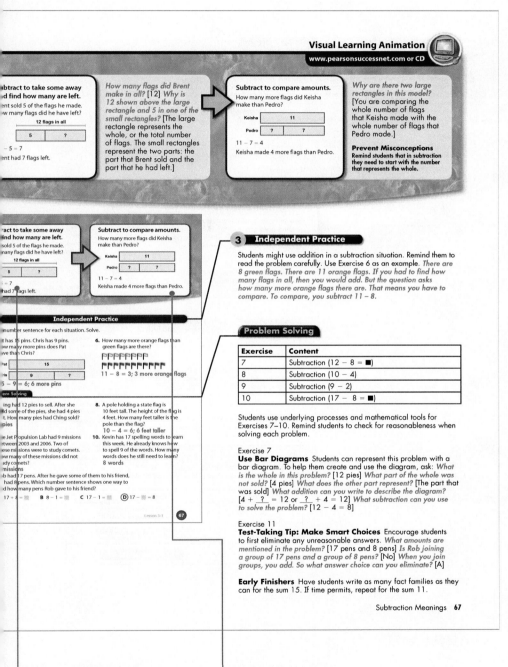

Visual Learning Animation
www.pearsonsuccessnet.com or CD

...btract to take some away
...d find how many are left.

...ent sold 5 of the flags he made.
...w many flags did he have left?

12 flags in all
| 5 | ? |

...– 5 = 7

...ent had 7 flags left.

How many flags did Brent make in all? [12] *Why is 12 shown above the large rectangle and 5 in one of the small rectangles?* [The large rectangle represents the whole, or the total number of flags. The small rectangles represent the two parts: the part that Brent sold and the part that he had left.]

Subtract to compare amounts.
How many more flags did Keisha make than Pedro?

| Keisha | 11 | |
| Pedro | ? | 7 |

11 – 7 = 4
Keisha made 4 more flags than Pedro.

Why are there two large rectangles in this model? [You are comparing the whole number of flags that Keisha made with the whole number of flags that Pedro made.]

Prevent Misconceptions
Remind students that in subtraction they need to start with the number that represents the whole.

...ract to take some away
...ind how many are left.
...sold 5 of the flags he made.
...any flags did he have left?

12 flags in all
| 5 | ? |

...– 7

...had 7 ...ags left.

Subtract to compare amounts.
How many more flags did Keisha make than Pedro?

| Keisha | 11 | |
| Pedro | ? | 7 |

11 – 7 = 4
Keisha made 4 more flags than Pedro.

Independent Practice

...number sentence for each situation. Solve.

...t has 15 pins. Chris has 9 pins.
...w many more pins does Pat
...ve than Chris?

| Pat | 15 |
| | 9 | ? |

...– 9 = 6; 6 more pins

Problem Solving

...ing had 12 pies to sell. After she
...d some of the pies, she had 4 pies
...t. How many pies had Ching sold?
...pies

...e Jet Propulsion Lab had 9 missions
...tween 2003 and 2006. Two of
...ese missions were to study comets.
...w many of these missions did not
...dy comets?
...missions

...b had 17 pens. After he gave some of them to his friend,
...d 8 pens. Which number sentence shows one way to
...d how many pens Rob gave to his friend?

17 + = ■   **B** 8 – 1 = ■   **C** 17 – 1 = ■   **(D)** 17 – 8 = ■

3 Independent Practice

Students might use addition in a subtraction situation. Remind them to read the problem carefully. Use Exercise 6 as an example. *There are 8 green flags. There are 11 orange flags. If you had to find how many flags in all, then you would add. But the question asks how many more orange flags there are. That means you have to compare. To compare, you subtract 11 – 8.*

Problem Solving

Exercise	Content
7	Subtraction (12 – 8 = ■)
8	Subtraction (10 – 4)
9	Subtraction (9 – 2)
10	Subtraction (17 – 8 = ■)

Students use underlying processes and mathematical tools for Exercises 7–10. Remind students to check for reasonableness when solving each problem.

Exercise 7
Use Bar Diagrams Students can represent this problem with a bar diagram. To help them create and use the diagram, ask: *What is the whole in this problem?* [12 pies] *What part of the whole was not sold?* [4 pies] *What does the other part represent?* [The part that was sold] *What addition can you write to describe the diagram?* [4 + ? = 12 or ? + 4 = 12] *What subtraction can you use to solve the problem?* [12 – 4 = 8]

Exercise 11
Test-Taking Tip: Make Smart Choices Encourage students to first eliminate any unreasonable answers. *What amounts are mentioned in the problem?* [17 pens and 8 pens] *Is Rob joining a group of 17 pens and a group of 8 pens?* [No] *When you join groups, you add. So what answer choice can you eliminate?* [A]

Early Finishers Have students write as many fact families as they can for the sum 15. If time permits, repeat for the sum 11.

Subtraction Meanings **67**

6. How many more orange flags than green flags are there?

ΡΡΡΡΡΡΡΡ
ΡΡΡΡΡΡΡΡΡΡΡ

11 – 8 = 3; 3 more orange flags

8. A pole holding a state flag is 10 feet tall. The height of the flag is 4 feet. How many feet taller is the pole than the flag?
10 – 4 = 6; 6 feet taller

10. Kevin has 17 spelling words to learn this week. He already knows how to spell 9 of the words. How many words does he still need to learn?
8 words

Independent Practice

67

Lesson 3-1

Bar Diagrams

Research says that bar diagrams can be a key to success in problem solving. Bar diagrams help students understand relationships between quantities in the problem, and this helps students choose a correct operation to solve the problem (Diezmann and English, 2001).

enVisionMATH™ provides:

- **An introduction to bar diagrams** in the Problem-Solving Handbook at the start of the year. See pages xvii–xxix in the Student Edition and in the Topic 1 Teacher's Edition.

- **Focused instruction on bar diagrams** in problem-solving lessons with titles such as "Draw a Picture and Write an Equation." See pages 98–100 in the Student Edition.

- **Infused reinforcement of bar diagrams** in regular lessons where bar diagrams enhance the visual learning support in the Visual Learning Bridge and in the practice exercises. See Exercise 5 at the left.

This **bar diagram** shows that you know the whole and one part and you need to find the other part.

This **bar diagram** shows that you know the larger amount and the smaller amount and need to find how much bigger the larger amount is.

Assessment and Prescription

Research says that ongoing assessment prevents misconceptions and provides valuable information to guide data-driven instruction (Vye et al., 1998).

enVisionMATH™ provides:

- **Do You Know How? Do You Understand?** within Student Edition lessons that help you assess both skills and conceptual understanding. See page T18.

- **Quick Check** at the end of lessons with multiple-choice items and a Writing to Explain item to help you monitor student progress.

- **Scoring Rubric** for the Writing to Explain item with four levels of performance described and four samples of student work included.

- **Prescription** for differentiated instruction.

---

4 Close/Assess and Differentiate

ELL STRATEGY Model Thinking Aloud

Close

Essential Understanding Some real-world problems involving joining, separating, part-part-whole, or comparison can be solved using subtraction. Fact families show addition and subtraction relationships. *In this lesson, you learned that you can write a subtraction number sentence to show a situation where you are taking away, comparing, or finding a missing addend. You also learned how to write fact families that relate addition and subtraction.*

Assess

Use the **Quick Check** to assess students' understanding.

Exercises 1–3 are worth 1 point each. Use the rubric to score Exercise 4.

Exercise 4
Writing to Explain Students should apply their understanding of subtraction to write a number sentence that fits a situation, and to explain how to find the difference.

ELL: Model Thinking Aloud Help students by modeling how to think about the problem. You can pose a series of guiding questions, such as: What numbers do I know? Which is the <u>whole</u> and which is the <u>part</u>? What do I have to find out? How can I solve it?

Student Samples
4-point answer The student writes a clear and complete explanation, gives a suitable number sentence, and finds the correct difference.

Tina has 15 magnets. She sells 8. I need to find how many magnets she has left. I have to subtract. I'll take away 8 (part) from 15 (whole) to find the part that Tina still has.
15 - 8 = □
I count on from 8 up to 15. I say 7 numbers, so that tells me that Tina has 7 magnets left.

3-point answer The student writes an adequate explanation, gives a number sentence, and finds the correct difference.

Tina starts with 15 magnets. She sells 8. I need to find 15 - 8 = ? I know to subtract because it's about selling part of the 15 she began with. 15 - 8 = 7. Tina has 7 magnets now.

2-point answer The student writes a vague explanation, with or without a number sentence, and finds the correct difference.

I have to find 15 - 8 because Tina sold 8 out of her 15 magnets. 15 - 8 = 7. So Tina still has 7 magnets.

1-point answer The student finds the correct difference with or without a number sentence, but with no explanation.

15 - 8 = 7. Tina has 7 magnets left.

Prescription for Differentiated Instruction
Use student work on the **Quick Check** to prescribe differentiated instruction.

Points	Prescription
0–4	Intervention
5–6	On-Level
7	Advanced

67A Topic 3

Teacher's Edition Lesson 3-1

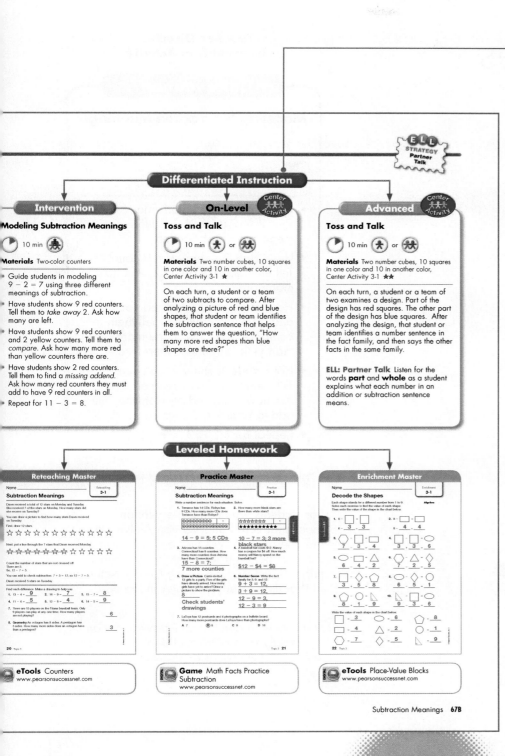

Differentiated Instruction

Intervention

Modeling Subtraction Meanings

⏱ 10 min 👤

Materials Two-color counters

- Guide students in modeling $9 - 2 = 7$ using three different meanings of subtraction.
- Have students show 9 red counters. Tell them to *take away* 2. Ask how many are left.
- Have students show 9 red counters and 2 yellow counters. Tell them to *compare*. Ask how many more red than yellow counters there are.
- Have students show 2 red counters. Tell them to find a *missing addend*. Ask how many red counters they must add to have 9 red counters in all.
- Repeat for $11 - 3 = 8$.

On-Level (Center Activity)

Toss and Talk

⏱ 10 min 👤 or 👥

Materials Two number cubes, 10 squares in one color and 10 in another color, Center Activity 3-1 ★

On each turn, a student or a team of two subtracts to compare. After analyzing a picture of red and blue shapes, that student or team identifies the subtraction sentence that helps them to answer the question, "How many more red shapes than blue shapes are there?"

Advanced (Center Activity)

Toss and Talk

⏱ 10 min 👤 or 👥

Materials Two number cubes, 10 squares in one color and 10 in another color, Center Activity 3-1 ★★

On each turn, a student or a team of two examines a design. Part of the design has red squares. The other part of the design has blue squares. After analyzing the design, that student or team identifies a number sentence in the fact family, and then says the other facts in the same family.

ELL: Partner Talk Listen for the words **part** and **whole** as a student explains what each number in an addition or subtraction sentence means.

Leveled Homework

Reteaching Master

Name _____ Reteaching 3-1

Subtraction Meanings

(worksheet)

Practice Master

Name _____ Practice 3-1

Subtraction Meanings

(worksheet)

Enrichment Master

Name _____ Enrichment 3-1

Decode the Shapes

(worksheet)

eTools Counters
www.pearsonsuccessnet.com

Game Math Facts Practice Subtraction
www.pearsonsuccessnet.com

eTools Place-Value Blocks
www.pearsonsuccessnet.com

Subtraction Meanings **67B**

Differentiated Instruction

Research says to give all students access to the same content but level the instruction based on how much support different students need (Cotton, 2001).

enVisionMATH™ provides:

- **Leveled activities** including an Intervention Activity that is teacher directed plus On-Level and Advanced Center Activities that can be done without teacher direction. See pages T22–T23.
- **Leveled homework** for Reteaching, Practice, and Enrichment.
- **Leveled digital resources** that include eTools, eTools Workshops, games, and MindPoint Quiz Show.

ELL Strategies

Research says there are a number of effective strategies for teaching math to English learners. These include strategies to enhance reading, writing, speaking, and listening (Cuevas et al., 1986).

enVisionMATH™ provides:

- **ELL strategies to support the Quick Check** including Provide Sentence Stems, Suggest Sequence, Suggest a Word List, Use Repetition, Model Thinking Aloud, and Rephrase.
- **ELL strategies to support the Center Activities** including Partner Talk and Report Back.

For more about ELL Strategies, see page T24.

Leveled Activities

Research says that students learn better when they are interested in what they're doing and engaged in activities with other students (Schwartz et al., 1999).

enVisionMATH™ provides:

Intervention Activities

- **Teacher-directed activity** at the end of each lesson.

Center Activities

- **Ready-made and independent** for each lesson.
- **Engaging** to help motivate students to do mathematical thinking and communication.
- **Leveled** so that different students do the same activity at different levels at the same time.
- **Easy-to-manage, independent work** that students can do by themselves without teacher involvement. There are seven different activity formats that repeat. Once students learn a format, they don't need directions again. See page T23.
- **Partner Talk** on each page that encourages students to share their thinking while they work.
- **Simple materials** provided in the Center Activities Manipulatives Kit that includes:

  number tiles with digits 0–9
  number cubes
  red and blue squares

- **Can be used over and over** since many are games and all include "If You Have More Time" at the end.
- **Can be used for ongoing review** because students can be directed to go back to them anytime.
- **Can be used year after year** because students don't write on the pages.

Teacher-Directed Intervention Activity

Intervention

Modeling Subtraction Meanings

🕐 10 min 👥

Materials Two-color counters

- Guide students in modeling $9 - 2 = 7$ using three different meanings of subtraction.
- Have students show 9 red counters. Tell them to *take away* 2. Ask how many are left.
- Have students show 9 red counters and 2 yellow counters. Tell them to *compare*. Ask how many more red than yellow counters there are.
- Have students show 2 red counters. Tell them to find a *missing addend*. Ask how many red counters they must add to have 9 red counters in all.
- Repeat for $11 - 3 = 8$.

For students who need intervention, a teacher-directed Intervention Activity like the one above gives you a chance to help students get on track right away. Then you might direct students to the Center Activities at that time or anytime later in the day.

Students who don't need intervention can go directly to the On-Level ★ or Advanced ★★ Center Activities as shown on page T23.

On-Level Center Activity
with Blackline Master

On-Level

Toss and Talk

 10 min or

Materials Two number cubes, 10 squares in one color and 10 in another color, Center Activity 3-1 ★

On each turn, a student or a team of two subtracts to compare. After analyzing a picture of red and blue shapes, that student or team identifies the subtraction sentence that helps them to answer the question, "How many more red shapes than blue shapes are there?"

Advanced Center Activity
with Blackline Master

Advanced

Toss and Talk

10 min ★ or ★★

Materials Two number cubes, 10 squares in one color and 10 in another color, Center Activity 3-1 ★★

On each turn, a student or a team of two examines a design. Part of the design has red squares. The other part of the design has blue squares. After analyzing the design, that student or team identifies a number sentence in the fact family, and then says the other facts in the same family.

ELL: Partner Talk Listen for the words **part** and **whole** as a student explains what each number in an addition or subtraction sentence means.

The seven Center Activity formats are:

- **Clip and Cover** A game in which players use number cubes and paper clips to select information and then answer questions, cover the answers in game spaces on a game board, and win when they cover four spaces in a row.

- **Display the Digits** An activity in which students answer questions, explain their thinking, and use number tiles to display their answers.

- **Quick Questions** A game in which players toss number cubes, answer questions that have answers from 1 to 6, remove cubes that match the answer, and win when both cubes are removed.

- **Teamwork** An activity in which students each pick a number to determine which student will explain which numbered step in a multi-step process involving skills or problem solving.

- **Think Together** An activity in which students are given a question and four answer choices and then pick number tiles to determine which student will discuss which answer choice.

- **Tic Tac Toe** A game with four Tic Tac Toe boards in which students toss number cubes, use an algebraic rule to compute with the numbers, and cover spaces on game boards where the answers appear.

- **Toss and Talk** A game in which a player tosses number cubes, explains how to answer a question next to the sum of the numbers, and wins by getting four connected rectangles on a four-by-four game board.

On-Level Center Activity ★

Advanced Center Activity ★★

Meeting Individual Needs

Research says that students learn best when instruction is designed to accommodate diverse types of learners (Fillmore and Meyer, 1996).

enVisionMATH™ provides support for:

English Language Learners (ELL)

- **For each topic** the Meeting Individual Needs feature provides topic-specific ELL considerations plus an ELL activity.

- **For each lesson** the **Interactive Learning** feature uses instructional strategies that help all students but are especially helpful to ELL students. These include:
  Use Drawings
  Use Photographs
  Use Common Objects
  Use Graphic Organizers
  Use Word Webs
  Use Number Webs
  Use Reference Charts
  Rephrase, Reword, and Simplify
  Use Repetition
  Total Physical Response
  Role-Play
  Use Pantomime
  Link to Familiar Contexts
  Link to Prior Knowledge
  Link to Other Subjects
  Small-Group Interaction
  Peer Questioning
  Use Practice Games
  Instruct in Small Steps
  Expand Student Responses

ELL strategies are also provided at the end of the lesson. See page T21. The pictorial nature of the **Visual Learning Bridge** in each lesson also helps ELL students. See page T18.

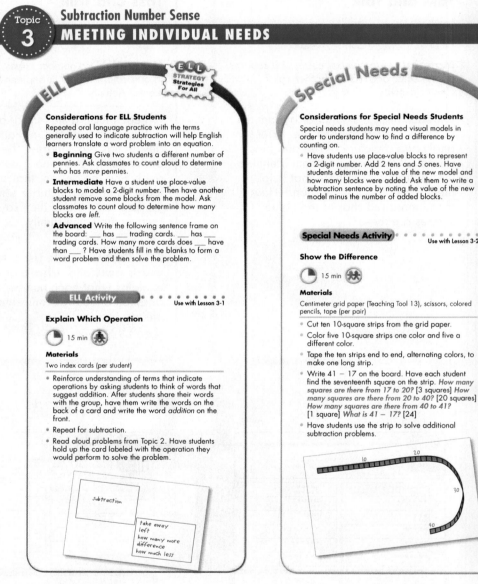

Topic 3

Subtraction Number Sense

MEETING INDIVIDUAL NEEDS

ELL — STRATEGY Strategies For All

Considerations for ELL Students

Repeated oral language practice with the terms generally used to indicate subtraction will help English learners translate a word problem into an equation.

- **Beginning** Give two students a different number of pennies. Ask classmates to count aloud to determine who has *more* pennies.
- **Intermediate** Have a student use place-value blocks to model a 2-digit number. Then have another student remove some blocks from the model. Ask classmates to count aloud to determine how many blocks are *left*.
- **Advanced** Write the following sentence frame on the board: ___ has ___ trading cards. ___ has ___ trading cards. How many more cards does ___ have than ___ ? Have students fill in the blanks to form a word problem and then solve the problem.

ELL Activity
Use with Lesson 3-1

Explain Which Operation

⏱ 15 min 👥

Materials
Two index cards (per student)

- Reinforce understanding of terms that indicate operations by asking students to think of words that suggest addition. After students share their words with the group, have them write the words on the back of a card and write the word *addition* on the front.
- Repeat for subtraction.
- Read aloud problems from Topic 2. Have students hold up the card labeled with the operation they would perform to solve the problem.

Special Needs

Considerations for Special Needs Students

Special needs students may need visual models in order to understand how to find a difference by counting on.

- Have students use place-value blocks to represent a 2-digit number. Add 2 tens and 5 ones. Have students determine the value of the new model and how many blocks were added. Ask them to write a subtraction sentence by noting the value of the new model minus the number of added blocks.

Special Needs Activity
Use with Lesson 3-2

Show the Difference

⏱ 15 min 👥

Materials
Centimeter grid paper (Teaching Tool 13), scissors, colored pencils, tape (per pair)

- Cut ten 10-square strips from the grid paper.
- Color five 10-square strips one color and five a different color.
- Tape the ten strips end to end, alternating colors, to make one long strip.
- Write 41 − 17 on the board. Have each student find the seventeenth square on the strip. *How many squares are there from 17 to 20?* [3 squares] *How many squares are there from 20 to 40?* [20 squares] *How many squares are there from 40 to 41?* [1 square] *What is 41 − 17?* [24]
- Have students use the strip to solve additional subtraction problems.

64C Topic 3

Meeting Individual Needs pages are provided at the beginning of each topic in the Teacher's Edition.

DIFFERENTIATED INSTRUCTION

  Below Level

Considerations for Below-Level Students
Using manipulatives to model regrouping will reinforce students' understanding of subtracting 2-digit numbers.

• Give a student $10 bills. Ask the student to hand you an amount that will require regrouping a $10 bill as ten $1 bills. Have classmates write a subtraction sentence that describes the actions.

• Have a volunteer use place-value blocks to model a 2-digit number. Ask another student to name a number less than the one modeled. Have the first student remove that number of blocks from the model.

Below-Level Activity • • • • • • •
Use with Lesson 3-3

Shopping Fun

🕐 20 min 👥

Materials
Price tags, bills (per pair)

• Have partners label six price tags with the following amounts: $27, $13, $18, $9, $22, and $7.

• Partner 1 plays the store clerk. Partner 2 plays the customer. Partner 2 selects a price tag and pays for it with two $20 bills.

• Partner 1 determines the amount of change by counting on to the price.

• Together, the partners write a subtraction sentence that shows the transaction.

• Players switch roles and play again. They continue playing until all price tags have been picked up.

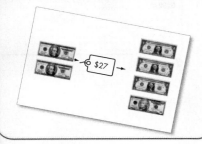

  Advanced

Considerations for Advanced Students
Challenge students to identify multiple methods of estimating a difference.

• Write a subtraction sentence involving two 3-digit numbers on the board. Have students estimate the difference first by rounding the number to the tens place and then using compatible numbers. Ask them to consider whether rounding or compatible numbers yielded an estimate closest to the actual answer.

• Have students write a subtraction sentence involving 3-digit numbers that yields the same estimate when rounded to the nearest ten or when using compatible numbers.

Advanced Activity • • • • • • •
Use with Lesson 3-4

The Best Estimate

🕐 15 min 👥

• Have each pair write 5 subtraction sentences involving 3-digit numbers.

• Pairs trade papers and estimate each difference using rounding to the nearest ten and then using compatible numbers.

• Pairs then find the exact answers. They compare the estimates to determine which process yielded an answer closest to the actual answer.

• Pairs compile results and analyze their findings.

• Ask students to explain to the class (or to their partner) which method yielded an estimate closest to the exact answer and why.

Special Needs
• **For each topic** the Meeting Individual Needs feature provides topic-specific considerations for special education students plus an activity.

• **For each lesson** the **Visual Learning Bridge** helps special education students focus on one idea at a time. See page T18.

Below Level
• **For each topic** the Meeting Individual Needs feature provides topic-specific considerations for below-level students plus an activity.

• **For each lesson** the program provides an Intervention Activity, a Reteaching Master, a reference to a digital resource appropriate for below-level students, and an Intervention Lesson in the Math Diagnosis and Intervention System.

Advanced
• **For each topic** the Meeting Individual Needs feature provides topic-specific considerations for advanced learners plus an activity.

• **For each lesson** the program provides an Advanced Center Activity, an Enrichment Master, and a reference to a digital resource appropriate for advanced students.

Problem-Solving Process

Research says explicit instruction in mathematical processes helps students become good problem solvers (Mayer and Wittrock, 1996).

en**Vision**MATH™ provides:

- **Problem-Solving Skills and Strategies**
  taught in problem-solving lessons:
  - Missing or Extra Information
  - Two-Question Problems
  - Multiple-Step Problems
  - Reasonableness
  - Make and Test Generalizations
  - Writing to Explain
  - Show the Problem
    - Draw a Picture
    - Make an Organized List
    - Make a Table
    - Make a Graph
    - Act It Out/Use Objects
  - Look for a Pattern
  - Try, Check, and Revise
  - Write a Number Sentence
  - Use Reasoning
  - Work Backward
  - Solve a Simpler Problem

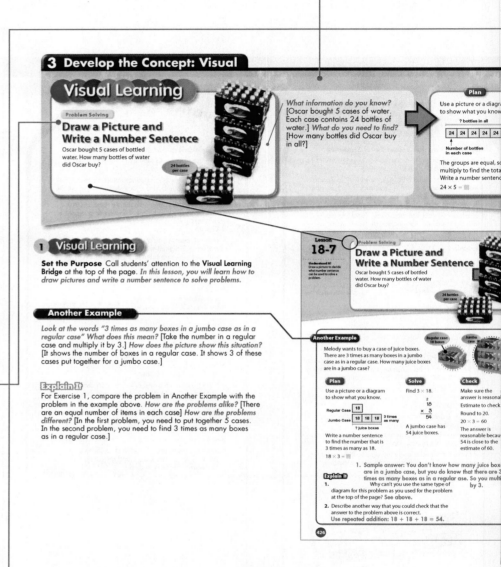

Teacher's Edition Lesson 18-7

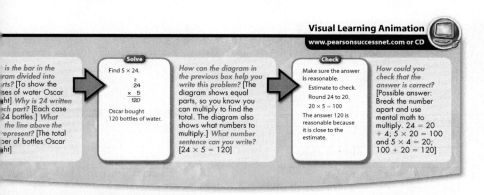

Visual Learning Animation
www.pearsonsuccessnet.com or CD

Solve

Find 5 × 24.
2
24
× 5
120

Oscar bought
120 bottles of water.

How can the diagram in the previous box help you write this problem? [The diagram shows equal parts, so you know you can multiply to find the total. The diagram also shows what numbers to multiply.] What number sentence can you write? [24 × 5 = 120]

Check

Make sure the answer is reasonable.
Estimate to check.
Round 24 to 20.
20 × 5 = 100
The answer 120 is reasonable because it is close to the estimate.

How could you check that the answer is correct? [Possible answer: Break the number apart and use mental math to multiply. 24 = 20 + 4; 5 × 20 = 100 and 5 × 4 = 20; 100 + 20 = 120]

---

is the bar in the
ram divided into
rts? [To show the
ses of water Oscar
ght] Why is 24 written
ch case
24 bottles.] What
the line above the
represent? [The total
er of bottles Oscar
ght]

Plan
icture or a diagram
r what you know.

bottles in all

24 24 24 24

r of bottles
case

ups are equal, so
y to find the total.
number sentence.

Solve

Find 5 × 24.
2
24
× 5
120

Oscar bought
120 bottles of water.

Check

Make sure the answer is reasonable.
Estimate to check.
Round 24 to 20.
20 × 5 = 100
The answer 120 is reasonable because it is close to the estimate.

Guided Practice*

u know HOW?

doll collection is displayed in
ows with 16 dolls in each row. How
any dolls are in the collection?
8 dolls

dolls in all

16 16 16 16 16 16

ber of dolls in each row

Do you UNDERSTAND?

2. Why do you multiply to solve Problem 1? See margin.

3. Write a problem that can be solved by drawing a picture. Draw the picture. Solve. Problems will vary.

Independent Practice

duardo has 36 football cards. He has 3 times
many baseball cards. How many baseball
ds does he have?

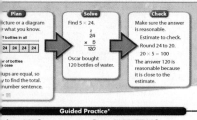

otball cards 36

aseball cards 36 36 36   3 times as many

7 baseball cards in all

8 cards
Noah has 95 books to
on 4 shelves. If he puts 24 books on each
elf, will all the books fit on the shelves?

? books fit   Yes, 4 × 24 = 96
24 24 24 24   and 95 < 96.

ber of books on each shelf

example, see Set F on page 433.

Lesson 18-7   **427**

swer

2. Sample response: You know the number of dolls in each row and the number of rows in the case. So you can multiply.

---

2 Guided Practice

The problem-solving strategy *Draw a Picture* can help students determine what number sentence to write to solve a problem. To review these strategies, refer students to the Problem-Solving Handbook.

Exercise 1
Error Intervention

If students have difficulty writing a number sentence from the diagram,

then help them relate the diagram to an operation. *What does the number in each part of the bar stand for?* [The number of dolls in each row] *Why are there 8 parts that show 16?* [There are 8 rows of dolls] *Are the rows equal?* [Yes] *So what could you do to find the total number of dolls in the case?* [Multiply 8 × 16; Add 16 + 16 + 16 + 16 + 16 + 16 + 16 + 16]

Reteaching For another example and more practice, assign **Reteaching** Set F on p. 433.

3 Independent Practice

Remind students that drawing a picture of the situation first can help them determine what number sentence to use to solve the problem.

Exercise 4
Use Bar Diagrams *In the bar diagram, what does the bar in the first row represent?* [The number of football cards Eduardo has] *Why are there 3 groups of 36 in the second row of the diagram?* [There are 3 times as many baseball cards as football cards.]

Exercise 5
Writing to Explain Encourage students to use words, pictures, numbers, or symbols to explain their solution. *How can you include a number sentence in your explanation?* [4 × 24 = 96] *Can Noah put 95 books on 4 shelves? Explain how you know.* [If 96 books fit on the shelves, Noah's 95 books will fit.]

Problem Solving: Draw a Picture and Write a Number Sentence   **427**

- **Phases in a problem-solving process** that are taught in problem-solving lessons.

  Read and Understand

  What am I trying to find?

  What do I know?

  Plan and Solve

  What strategy or strategies should I try?

  Can I show the problem?

  How will I solve the problem?

  What is the answer?

  Look Back and Check

  Did I check my work?

  Is my answer reasonable?

- **Problem-based instruction** through Pose the Problem in Interactive Learning. See page T17.

- **Bar diagrams** that help students show visual representations of quantitative relationships for a variety of problems. See page T19.

- **Problem-Solving Handbook** in front of the student book that is a resource students can go back to throughout the year. It includes:

  Problem-Solving Process
  Using Bar Diagrams
  Problem-Solving Strategies
  Writing to Explain
  Problem-Solving Recording Sheet

A solid foundation in problem solving and algebra . . .

Problem-Solving Practice

Research says that students need practice with a variety of types of problems (Nesher, 1988).

enVisionMATH™ provides:

- **Problem-solving practice exercises** throughout the book including:

   Think About the Process
   Reasonableness
   Writing to Explain
   Draw It
   Write a Problem
   Strategy Focus

- **Problem-Solving Recording Sheet** that helps students record their thinking.

Name _____   Teaching Tool 1

Problem-Solving Recording Sheet

Problem:

Find?	Know?	Strategies?
		Show the Problem
		☐ Draw a Picture
		☐ Make an Organized List
		☐ Make a Table
		☐ Make a Graph
		☐ Act It Out/Use Objects
		☐ Look for a Pattern
		☐ Try, Check, Revise
		☐ Write an Equation
		☐ Use Reasoning
		☐ Work Backwards
		☐ Solve a Simpler Problem

Show the Problem?	Solution?

Answer?	Check? Reasonable?

Teaching Tools • 1

Teaching Tool 1 Master found in the Teaching Tools pouch in the Teacher Resource Masters

---

3 Develop the Concept

Exercise	Content
4	Draw a Picture and Write a Number Sentence
5	Draw a Picture and Write a Number Sentence
6	Draw a Picture and Write a Number Sentence
7	Multiple-Step Problems
8	Multiple-Step Problems
9	Subtraction (60 − 25)
10	Draw a Picture and Write a Number Sentence
11a	Multiplication (3 × 24, 5 × 24)
11b	Addition (72 + 120)
12	Multiplication (23 × 4)
13	Addition (46 + 25 + 34)

Students use underlying processes and mathematical tools for Exercises 4–13. Remind students to check for reasonableness when solving each problem.

Exercises 6–8
Language of Math: Read Data Sources *What does the title tell you about the table?* [It shows how many calories are used in 1 minute] *In which row do you find the number of calories used in 1 minute of running?* [In the fourth row]

Exercise 9
Problem-Solving Strategy: Act It Out Encourage students to use a clock to first find how many minutes are in an hour. *What do you need to find?* [How many more minutes Frank spent riding his bike than rollerblading] *Frank rode his bike for one hour. How many minutes are in one hour?* [60 minutes] *How many minutes did he Rollerblade?* [25 minutes]

Rode Bike 60 minutes

25	?
Went Rollerblading	? more minutes

Exercise 12
Test-Taking Tip: Understand the Question Remind students to look for important words. *Note that the question is asking for how much he earned this week.*

Independent Practice

The table shows about how many calories a 150-pound adult uses doing different activities. Use the table for 6–8.

6. Martha's mother went jogging for 15 minutes. How many calories did she use?
120 calories ? calories in all

| | | | | | | | | | | | | | | | |
Number of calories used each minute

Calories Used in 1 Minute

Activity	Number of Cal
Swimming	10
Jogging	8
Rollerblading	4
Running	9

7. Mr. Lee ran for 25 minutes. Then he swam for 20 minutes. How many calories did he use in all?
425 calories

8. Miss Nunez plans to swim for 15 minutes every day. How m calories will she use in a week
1,050 calories

9. Frank rode his bike for an hour. Then he went rollerblading for 25 minutes. How many more minutes did he spend riding his bike than rollerblading? 35 minutes

10. The U.S. Department of Health reports that many children spend about 32 hours each week in front of a computer screen. About how many hours is that in a month? About 120 hours   1 month 4 weeks.

11. Stacy has 3 bags of red beads. Cynthia has 2 more bags than Stacy. There are 24 beads in each bag.
a How many beads does each girl have? Stacy: 72 beads; Cynthia: 120
b How many beads do the girls have all together? 192 beads

Think About the Process

12. Mike earns $4 an hour doing yard work. He worked 12 hours last week and 23 hours this week. Which number sentence shows how much he earned this week?
A $23 + $12 = ▦
B 12 × $4 = ▦
C 23 × $4 = ▦
D (23 × $4) ÷ 7 = ▦

13. Katy read 46 pages of a book Monday. She read 25 pages o Tuesday. She still had 34 page read. Which number sentence how many pages are in the b
A 46 + 25 = ▦
B 46 − 34 = ▦
C (46 + 25) − 34 = ▦
D 46 + 25 + 34 = ▦

428

---

428   Topic 18

Teacher's Edition Lesson 18-7

Algebra

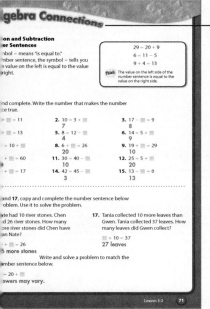

Algebra Connections

Addition and Subtraction Number Sentences

A number sentence that includes the equals symbol indicates that two numbers or expressions are equal. Students probably are most familiar with number sentences such as $9 + 4 = 13$ in the Examples box, where a sum or difference is on the right of the equals sign. Using the other examples, help them see that a sum or difference can also be written to the left of the equals sign.

Exercise 1
What is missing in this number sentence? [An addend.] *Suppose I write a 5 for the missing addend. Would the number sentence be true?* [No] *Why not?* [Because 9 + 5 is equal to 14, not 11.] *What addend could I write to make the number sentence true?* [2] *Why?* [Because 9 + 2 is equal to 11.]

Exercise 2
Error Intervention

If students simply add the given numbers and write the sum,

then have them read the number sentence aloud and restate it as a question. *Read each symbol aloud as I point to it.* [Ten, is equal to, three, plus, a missing number] *How can you change that sentence into a question?* [Sample answer: Ten is equal to three plus what number?] *What is the answer?* [7]

Exercise 18
Language of Math: Understand Math Symbols *What operation symbol do you see in this number sentence?* [A plus sign, for addition] *What is being added?* [20 and a missing number] *Do you know the sum when you add 20 and the missing number?* [Yes. The sum is 48.] *In what situations might you have to find that missing number?* [Sample answer: You want to buy something that costs $48, you have $20, and you want to know how much more money you need.]

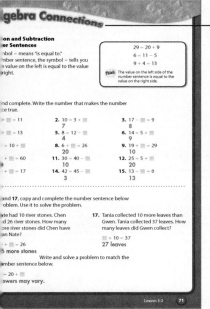

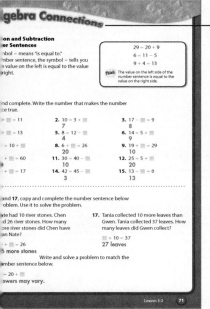

Research says that good conceptual development in algebra readiness results in better performance in algebra in middle school and high school (Behr, Harel, Post, and Lesh, 1992).

enVisionMATH™ provides:

- **Algebra Connections** pages that provide more algebra reinforcement and practice with scaffolded support.

- **Algebra topics and lessons** that provide a strong foundation in algebraic concepts.

- **Algebra exercises integrated into regular lessons** that connect algebra to other strands and reinforce algebraic thinking throughout the book.

Integrated support to help students access math as a language . . .

Vocabulary

Research says mathematics is like a language and some techniques used to learn language can be used to learn the language of math (Paris and Cunningham, 1996).

enVisionMATH™ provides:

- **Vocabulary Cards** in the Teacher Resource Masters that have words on one side and definitions on the other.

- **Connections to Everyday Vocabulary** in front of each topic that connect math vocabulary to everyday vocabulary (a link to prior knowledge) in ways that help students remember what the math words mean.

- **Vocabulary Activities** in front of each topic that help students solidify their understanding of math terms.

- **Vocabulary** in lesson notes in the Teacher's Edition.

Topic 3

Subtraction Number Sense
THE LANGUAGE OF MATH

The Language of Subtraction Number Sense
In this topic, students use mental math strategies to find the difference of 2-digit numbers. They also use estimation strategies to determine the reasonableness of an answer. Understanding the mathematical terminology used to identify problem-solving strategies will help students recognize whether an exact answer or an estimate is needed to solve a problem. The following terms will all be encountered in this topic and are included in the vocabulary card masters.

Review Vocabulary	New Vocabulary
add	**difference**
round	
subtract	

difference

Cards can always be used as flash cards and for playing a matching game. Another option is to say two numbers aloud, hold up a card, and have students perform the action named.

*Making **real-life connections** to vocabulary can strengthen students' understanding of mathematical terms.*

Difference
When you compare items, you say how they are different. One **difference** between a pair of numbers is the amount by which one number is greater than the other number.

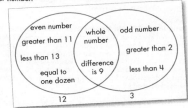

Symbol
A symbol is a picture, letter, digit, or icon that represents a word, phrase, or idea. There are many kinds of symbols. In math, the symbol = means "is equal to," the symbol > means "is greater than," and the symbol < means "is less than." You see many kinds of symbols in the real world. A stop sign means "stop moving" and a green traffic light means "**go.**"

Estimate or Exact Answer
On a large piece of poster board or chart paper, have students write the number sentence 64 − 29. Ask students to solve and record the exact answer. Then have them write the problem with rounded numbers to estimate the difference. Have students write the following labels on the appropriate parts of their papers: *round, difference, estimate,* and *exact answer.*

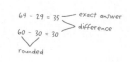

Teacher's Edition

Reading Comprehension and Problem Solving

Research says reading comprehension plays an important role in understanding word problems in math (Mayer and Wittrock, 1996).

en**Vision**MATH™ provides:

- **Reading comprehension** strategies at the start of each topic along with questions to guide comprehension using a Problem-Solving Recording Sheet.

- **Understanding Relationships and Reading Data Sources** in lesson notes in the Teacher's Edition.

Questions to Guide Comprehension

Some students can read a word problem (decode the words) but need help to identify the order of important ideas described in the problem. Use questions like the ones shown here to guide comprehension. (Draw visual images)

From Lesson 3-3 Exercise 10

Suppose a coat has an original price of $74 and it is on sale for $18 less than the original price. What is the sale price of the coat? How can you use mental math to solve this problem?

1. *What question do you need to answer?*
   [What is the sale price of the coat?]

2. *What* **caused** *the original price of the coat to change?*
   [The coat went on sale.]

3. *How could* **you represent the information in a bar diagram?**
   [The line above the bar is the original price of the coat, $74. One part of the bar should be $18 and the other part is the sale price.]

4. *How could you change each number to make a simpler problem?*
   [I can add 2 to each number to make the problem $76 – $20]

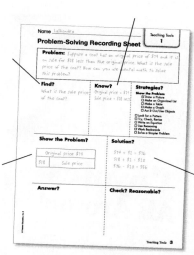

Writing to Explain

The "Writing to Explain" exercises (pp. 69, 70, 72, 73, 75, 76, and 78) help students clarify their thinking and show that they understand. In some of these exercises, students are asked to consider multiple methods of solving a problem. Some students may have the misconception that there is only one correct method of solving a problem. Stress that many problems can be solved in multiple ways.

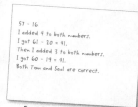

57 – 16
I added 4 to both numbers.
I got 61 – 20 = 41.
Then I added 3 to both numbers.
I got 60 – 19 = 41.
Both Tom and Saul are correct.

From Lesson 3-3, Exercise 32

WorldScapes Reader™

Magic Squares and More Additional activities and problem suggestions for Lesson 3-5 can be found on pp. 4–5 of *Magic Squares and More.*

The Language of Math   **64F**

— For Math and Literature, see pages T32–T35.

Written and Oral Language in Math

Research says writing, speaking, and listening are important aspects of math literacy (Pike, 2003).

en**Vision**MATH™ provides:

- **Writing, talking, or listening support** at the start of each topic.

- **Writing to Explain** in lesson notes in the Teacher's Edition.

Math and Literature: MathStart®

Research says literature is an engaging way to help children access math concepts (Hong, 1996).

enVisionMATH™ provides:

- **MathStart® readers by Stuart J. Murphy,** which are fiction books that teach math concepts through stories and visual learning strategies (sold separately from enVisionMATH).

- **Engaging stories and illustrations** in the MathStart books that hold students' interest and show how math is relevant to their lives.

- **Accessible text** that is age appropriate.

- **Visual models** that enhance conceptual understanding.

The books in the Math Library are also available in Spanish.

A Conversation with Stuart J. Murphy

Stuart J. Murphy's background as an expert in visual learning, which inspired his work on the MathStart series, has also played an integral role in the development of the *en**Vision**MATH* program.

Q: What is visual learning?

A: Visual learning is the acquisition, assimilation, and application of information through visual stimuli, such as charts, graphs, diagrams, illustrations, and photographs.

Q: How is visual learning applied to educational books?

A: Visual learning supports instruction. This includes hardworking pictures with a purpose, information organized in digestible chunks, visual models that demonstrate concepts, the visual-verbal balance of a page, and graphic design that shows hierarchies and connections to reinforce important relationships between ideas.

Q: Why is visual learning important in math?

A: Visual learning supports the development of critical-thinking skills and problem-solving capabilities so that students perform better in math. It builds bridges from concrete to abstract representations. Purposeful pictures include images that show the information needed to solve real-world problems. Digestible chunks give students a chance to focus on an individual math concept or a single step in a math procedure. Visual models help students understand math concepts. And, the arrangement of visuals and text on a page shows how multiple concepts or ideas work together, so that students see math as cohesive and not just a set of unrelated steps.

Books in the Grade K–2 Math Libraries

Grade K
- Animals on Board
- Every Buddy Counts
- Jack the Builder
- Just Enough Carrots
- Same Old Horse

Grade 1
- A Fair Bear Share
- Leaping Lizards
- 100 Days of Cool
- Spunky Monkeys on Parade
- Super Sand Castle Saturday

Grade 2
- Coyotes All Around
- Elevator Magic
- Missing Mittens
- Game Time!
- Shark Swimathon

For a complete list of books in the MathStart series appropriate for students of various ages, see the MathStart® Bibliography on p. T174.

Math and Literature: WorldScapes™

Research says non-fiction literature is an effective way to reinforce real-world problem solving and applications (Dreher, 2000).

enVisionMATH™ provides:

- **WorldScapes™ math content readers** which are beautiful non-fiction books that include passages about real-world math along with comprehension questions.

- **Cross-cultural, cross-curricular** literacy resource that interweaves math skills and concepts with facts about the history, environment, and culture of specific countries.

- **Engaging contexts** that include interesting information with appealing pictures. A child from each country introduces the book and poses questions about the main topic.

- **References to the books** in each topic on The Language of Math page in the Teacher's Edition. See page T31.

- **Guided Problem Solving Masters** with teacher notes that come with the books.

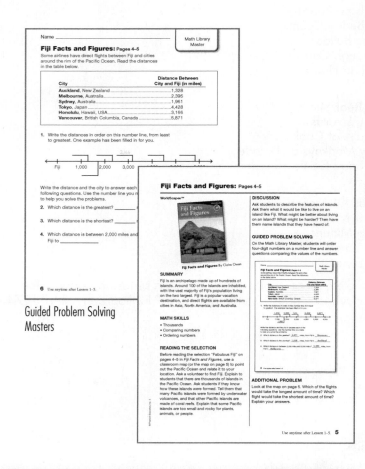

Guided Problem Solving Masters

Fabulous Fiji

Fiji is an archipelago (AR kuh PEL uh go) in the Pacific Ocean. It has 322 islands that are large enough for people to live on, but only 106 islands actually have people living on them. Fiji has a population of more than 800,000 people. Almost nine-tenths of Fijians live on the two largest islands.

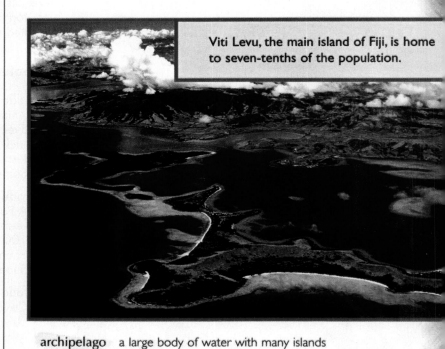

Viti Levu, the main island of Fiji, is home to seven-tenths of the population.

archipelago   a large body of water with many islands

4

WorldScapes Math Content Readers

Fiji is a popular place for vacations. There are direct flights to Fiji from New Zealand and other countries around the rim of the Pacific Ocean.

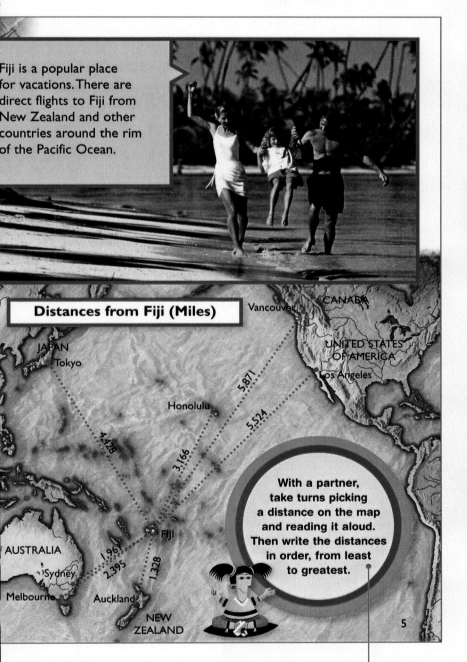

Distances from Fiji (Miles)

Vancouver

CANADA

JAPAN
Tokyo

UNITED STATES OF AMERICA

Los Angeles

5,871

Honolulu

5,524

4,428

3,166

With a partner, take turns picking a distance on the map and reading it aloud. Then write the distances in order, from least to greatest.

AUSTRALIA

Sydney

FIJI

1,961

2,395

1,328

Melbourne

Auckland

NEW ZEALAND

5

Questions that reinforce content taught in the program

Below Zero
WORLDSCAPES
Arctic
Written by Claire Owen

Arctic

Fiji Facts and Figures
WORLDSCAPES
Pacific Islands
Written by Claire Owen

Pacific Islands

Keeping Count
WORLDSCAPES
India
Written by Claire Owen

India

Magic Squares and More
WORLDSCAPES
China
Written by Claire Owen

China

Perfect Patterns
WORLDSCAPES
South Africa
Written by Claire Owen

South Africa

Rainforest Math
WORLDSCAPES
Costa Rica
Written by Claire Owen

Costa Rica

Surviving the Odds
WORLDSCAPES
Australia
Written by Claire Owen

Australia

Frequent Progress Monitoring

Research says frequent progress monitoring gives students valuable feedback and course corrections, while giving teachers information about students that can guide instruction (Black and Black, 1998).

enVisionMATH™ provides:

- **Frequent assessment** opportunities as shown in the white boxes in the flowchart below.

Key

- Student Edition
- Teacher's Edition

Blackline Masters

- (A) Teacher Resource Masters
- (B) ISAT Mathematics Test Prep
- (C) Illinois Topic Tests in ISAT Mathematics Test Format
- (D) Illinois Math Diagnosis and Intervention System

Digital Resources

- (A) ExamView® (See page T39.)
- (B) SuccessTracker (See page T39.)

White Boxes = Assessment

Black Boxes = Intervention

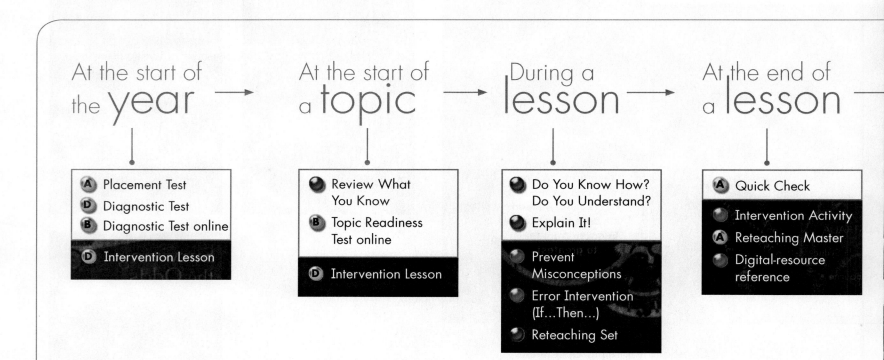

At the start of the year →
- (A) Placement Test
- (D) Diagnostic Test
- (B) Diagnostic Test online
- (D) Intervention Lesson

At the start of a topic →
- Review What You Know
- (B) Topic Readiness Test online
- (D) Intervention Lesson

During a lesson →
- Do You Know How? Do You Understand?
- Explain It!
- Prevent Misconceptions
- Error Intervention (If...Then...)
- Reteaching Set

At the end of a lesson →
- (A) Quick Check
- Intervention Activity
- (A) Reteaching Master
- Digital-resource reference

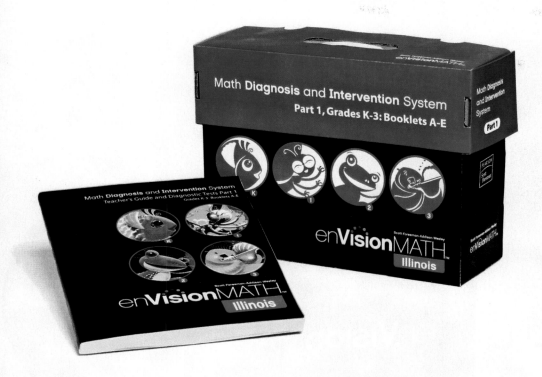

Varied Intervention Resources

Research says timely intervention when needed and in different modalities is an important part of helping all students succeed in math (Bell, 1982).

en**Vision**MATH.™ provides:

- **Frequent intervention** in a variety of formats as shown in the black boxes in the flowchart below.

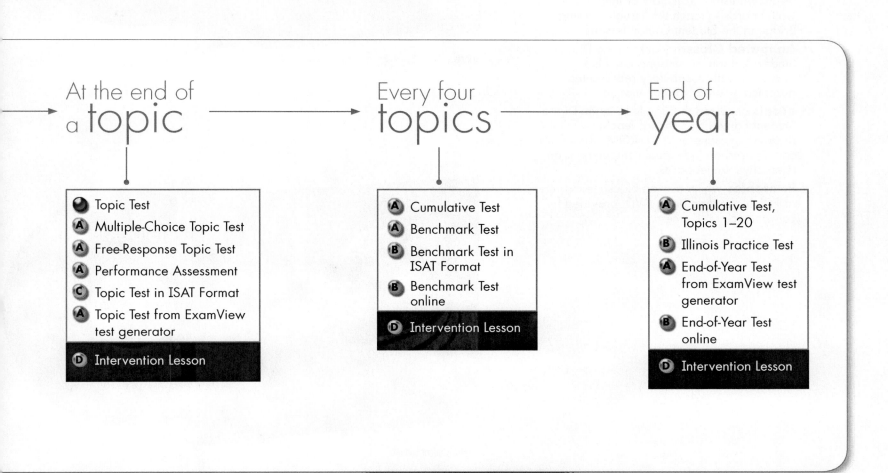

At the end of
a topic

- Topic Test
- (A) Multiple-Choice Topic Test
- (A) Free-Response Topic Test
- (A) Performance Assessment
- (C) Topic Test in ISAT Format
- (A) Topic Test from ExamView test generator
- (D) Intervention Lesson

Every four
topics

- (A) Cumulative Test
- (A) Benchmark Test
- (B) Benchmark Test in ISAT Format
- (B) Benchmark Test online
- (D) Intervention Lesson

End of
year

- (A) Cumulative Test, Topics 1–20
- (B) Illinois Practice Test
- (A) End-of-Year Test from ExamView test generator
- (B) End-of-Year Test online
- (D) Intervention Lesson

Your Digital Environment

Research says computers and the Internet increase students' and teachers' access to math concepts and resources, provide greater potential for customization, and enable students to work in different modalities (Cognition and Technology Group at Vanderbilt University, 1996).

enVisionMATH™ provides:

Digital Student and Teacher's Edition

- **Student Editions and Teacher's Editions online and on CD-ROM** for anytime-anywhere access and convenience, with optional audio.

- **Visual Learning Animations** that can be shown using projectors or interactive whiteboards to teach the Visual Learning Bridge in the Student Edition lessons.

- **Animated Glossary** links in the Digital Student Edition, so students can click to access math vocabulary represented graphically, often with animation.

- **eTools** accessed through links in the Digital Student Edition and Digital Teacher's Edition or standing alone on a CD-ROM. The eTools can be used on individual computers or on interactive whiteboards.

- **Printables** which are the blackline masters as PDF files online or on DVD, provided for convenience and access.

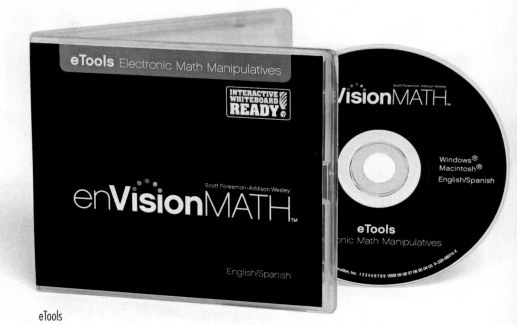

eTools

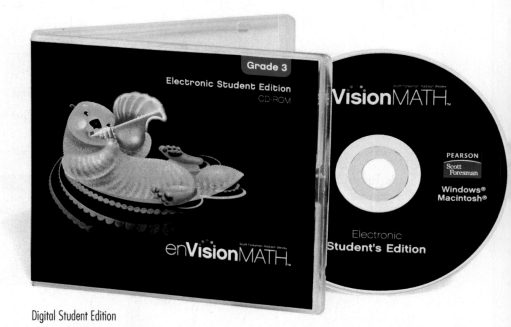

Digital Student Edition

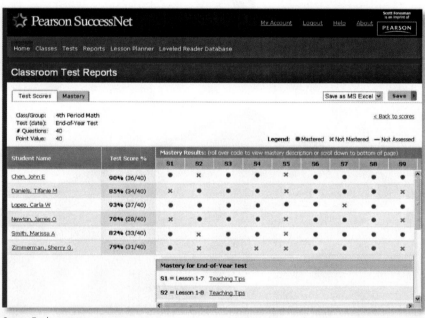

SuccessTracker

SuccessTracker

- **Student, teacher, and parent home pages,** where teachers assign tests to students and view reports, where students access the tests assigned to them, and where parents can view their child's progress on tests.

- **Tests** including beginning-of-year diagnostic tests, topic readiness tests, end-of-topic tests, end-of-year tests, and benchmark tests. All topic tests include a test and a retest.

- **Reports** on individual students and classes, showing mastery and nonmastery of the content tested thus far.

- **Prescriptions** in reports, indicating the lesson pages and print resources that provide review and reteaching of nonmastered content.

Digital Resources on CD-ROMs

- **MindPoint Quiz Show** that provides students with additional practice and remediation at the end of each topic.

- **Games** that provide students with additional practice and remediation.

- **ExamView®** that provides teachers with banks of questions, a test-construction tool, and a test-question editor. Teachers can create and print tests, quizzes, and practice pages on any combination of lessons, or topics.

- **Student Editions and Teacher's Editions** that provide the student or teacher pages.

Exam View® Assessment Suite

Everything You Need in One Place

en**Vision**MATH™ saves teachers prep time by providing all the comprehensive materials you need to plan and teach in one place.

- **Materials easy to store and easy to find** with everything in one container and clearly labeled—including blackline masters that are filed in order of use with their corresponding Teacher's Editions and have tabs down the side to help pages stay organized.

- **Materials designed for durability** with Topic Teacher's Editions that are only used for the length of one topic each year (so they won't fall apart as the years go by). Blackline masters are stored in sturdy plastic pouches.

Teacher's Edition and
Resources Package

enVisionMATH™ Teacher's Edition
and Resources Package includes:

- **Overview and Implementation Guide**

- **20 Topic Teacher's Editions**
  Materials that are compact, lightweight, and easy
  to take home with a Teacher's Edition followed by
  Teacher Resource Masters for each topic.

- **20 Topic Teacher Resource Master Pouches**
  Blackline masters stored in topic pouches.

  Center Activities

  Vocabulary Cards

  Home-School Connection

  Lesson resources with all pages
  for a lesson kept together

  Daily Spiral Review

  Problem of the Day

  Interactive Learning Recording Sheet

  Quick Check

  Reteaching

  Practice

  Enrichment

  Assessment

- **Topics 1–20 Teaching Tool Masters**
  such as grids, number lines, etc.

Overview and Implementation Guide

Topic Teacher's Edition

Topic Teacher Resource Masters in pouches

Blackline masters easy to copy
with pages that don't need to be
torn out of a book of masters. This
pouch is directly behind the Topic 1
Teacher's Edition.

Comprehensive Program Components

en**Vision**MATH™ program components for Grade 3 include:

Student Resources

- Student Edition
- Interactive Homework Workbook

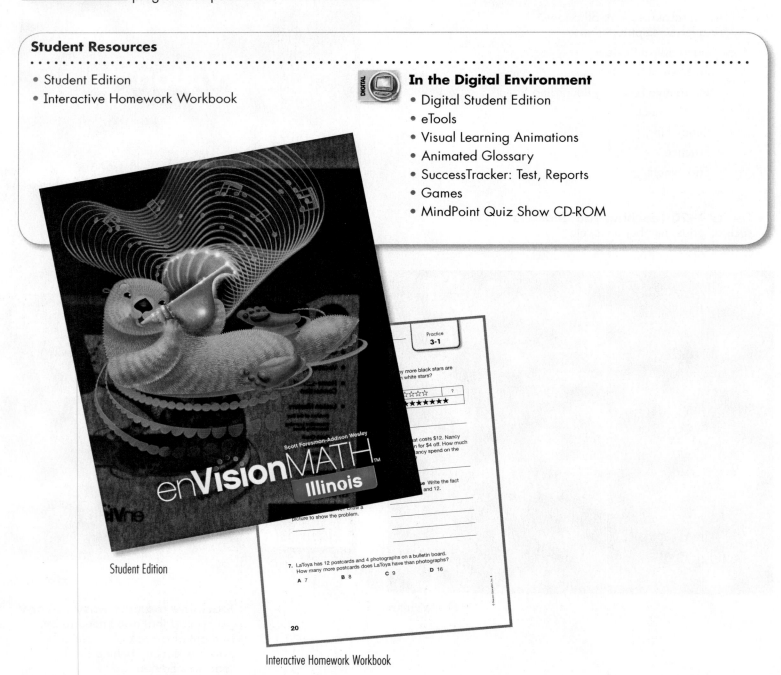

In the Digital Environment

- Digital Student Edition
- eTools
- Visual Learning Animations
- Animated Glossary
- SuccessTracker: Test, Reports
- Games
- MindPoint Quiz Show CD-ROM

Scott Foresman-Addison Wesley

en**Vision**MATH™ Illinois

Student Edition

Practice
3-1

7. LaToya has 12 postcards and 4 photographs on a bulletin board.
How many more postcards does LaToya have than photographs?

A 7   B 8   C 9   D 16

20

Interactive Homework Workbook

Teacher's Edition and Resources Package

- Overview and Implementation Guide
- Topic Teacher's Editions
- Topic Teacher Resource Masters
    - Daily Spiral Review
    - Problem of the Day
    - Interactive Learning Recording Sheet
    - Quick Check
    - Center Activities
    - Reteaching
    - Practice
    - Enrichment
    - Vocabulary Cards
    - Home-School Connection
    - Assessment
- Topics 1–20 Teaching Tool Masters

In the Digital Environment

- Digital Teacher's Edition
- Printables
- Visual Learning Animations
- SuccessTracker: Tests, Reports, Prescriptions
- ExamView® Test Generator CD-ROM

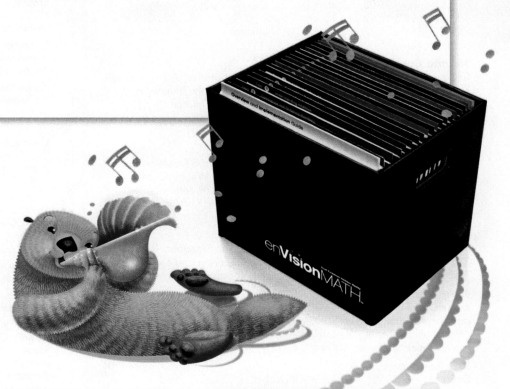

Additional Resources

- Visual Learning Bridge Transparencies
- ISAT Mathematics Test Prep
- Illinois Topic Tests in ISAT Mathematics Test Format
- Illinois Math Diagnosis and Intervention System
- Math Library with Guided Problem Solving

Manipulatives

- Classroom Manipulatives Kit
- Teacher's Overhead Manipulatives Kit
- Individual Student Manipulatives Kit
- Center Activities Manipulatives Kit

Professional Development

- Math Across the Grades
- Needs Assessment
- Professional Development Series

RESEARCH BIBLIOGRAPHY

Scientific research-based curriculum and instruction . . .

Samples of Author Research and Other References

Randall Charles
Charles, R. I., and Lester, F. K. (1984). "An Evaluation of a Process-oriented Instructional Program in Mathematical Problem Solving at Grades 5 and 7." *Journal for Research in Mathematics Education.* 15(1), pp. 15–34.

Janet H. Caldwell
Caldwell, J., & Goldin, G. (1979) "Variables Affecting 'Word Problem' Difficulty in Elementary School Mathematics," *Journal for Research in Mathematics Education,* November 1979, 10 (5), 323–326.

Mary Cavanagh
Navigations Series, *PreK–Gr. 2 Number and Operations* ©2004, *Measurement* ©2003, *Algebra* ©2001, *Data* ©2003, *Geometry* ©2002, and *Problem Solving and Reasoning Pre K–K* ©2003, *Grade 1* ©2004, *Grade 2* ©2004. Reston, VA: National Council of Teachers of Mathematics.

Juanita Copley
Copley, J. V. (2004). "The Early Childhood Collaborative: A Professional Development Model to Communicate and Implement the Standards." In D. Clements & J. Arama (Eds.), *Engaging Young Children in Mathematics: Standards for Early Childhood Mathematics.* New Jersey: Lawrence Erlbaum Associates, pp. 401–414.

Warren Crown
Crown, W. D. (2004). "Using Technology to Enhance a Problem-Based Approach to Teaching: What Will and What Will Not Work." In Frank K. Lester & Randall I. Charles (Eds.), *Teaching Mathematics through Problem Solving.* Reston, VA: National Council of Teachers of Mathematics, 2004.

Skip Fennell
Fennell, F. and Graham, K. (2001). "Principles and Standards for School Mathematics and Teacher Education: Preparing and Empowering Teachers," *School Science and Mathematics,* October 2001.

Alma Ramirez
Barnett-Clarke, C. and Ramirez, A. (2004). "Language pitfalls and pathways to mathematics." In Rita Rubenstein (Ed.), *Perspectives on Mathematics Teaching.* Reston, VA: National Council of Teachers of Mathematics Yearbook, 2004.

Kay Sammons
Sammons, K. (1992). Co-author with Kobett, B., Heiss, J., and Fennell, F. "Linking Assessment to Instruction," *Arithmetic Teacher,* February 1992.

Jane Schielack
Schielack, J. F. and Chancellor, D. (1994). "Stop, Look, Listen, and Produce: Building Reflective Thinking into Teacher Inservice." *Professional Development for Teachers of Mathematics: 1994 Yearbook* (pp. 304–307). Reston, VA: National Council of Teachers of Mathematics.

William Tate
Tate, W. F. and Rousseau, C. (2002). "Access and Opportunity: The Political and Social Context of Mathematics Education." In L. English (Ed.), *International Handbook of Research in Mathematics Education.* Mahwah, New Jersey: Lawrence Erlbaum Associates, pp. 271–300.

John Van de Walle
Van de Walle, John A. (2003). "Designing and Selecting Problem-Based Tasks," in Frank K. Lester, Jr., and Randall I. Charles (Eds.), *Teaching Mathematics through Problem Solving: Prekindergarten–Grade 6.* Reston, VA: National Council of Teachers of Mathematics, 2003.

Research Referenced in the Teacher's Editions

Behr, M. J., Harel, G., Post, T., & Lesh, R. "Rational Number, Ratio, and Proportion." In D. A. Grouws (Ed.), *Handbook of Research on Mathematics Teaching and Learning* (1992), pp. 296–333. (See Teacher's Edition page T29.)

Behr, Merlyn, J., Wachsmuth, Ipke. Post, Thomas R,. Lesh, Richard. *Journal for Research in Mathematics Education,* Vol. 15, No. 5 (1984), pp. 323–34

Bell, AW. "Diagnosing Students' Misconceptions." *The Australian Mathematics Teacher* 1 (1982): 6–10. (See Teacher's Edition page T37.)

Black, P. & William, D. "Assessment and Classroom Learning." In *Assessment and Education. Special Issue of Assessment in Education: Principles, Policy, and Practice.* 5 (1) (1998): 7–75. (See Teacher's Edition page T36.)

Brophy, J. & Good, T. L. "Teacher Behavior and Student Achievement." In M. C. Wittrock (Ed.), *Handbook of Research on Teaching* New York: Macmillan. (1986): 328–375. (See Teacher's Edition page T17.)

Carpenter, T.P., Coburn, R. Reys, and J Wilson. "Notes from National Assessment: Recognizing and Naming Solids." *Arithmetic Teacher,* 23 (1976), pp. 62–66. (See Teachers Edition pp. 234A)

Carpenter, T, and E. Fennema. "Cognitively Guided Instruction: Building on the Knowledge of Students and Teachers." *International Journal of Educational Research. Special Issue: The Case of Mathematics in the United States.* W. Secada (Ed.), (1992), pp. 457–470. (See Teacher's Edition page T18.)

Choate, L. D., and J. K. Okey. "Graphically Speaking: Primary Level Graphing Experiences." *In Teaching Statistics and Probability.* Edited by A. P. Shulte and J. Smart, pp. 33–40. Reston, VA: National Council of Teachers of Mathematics, 1981. (See Teacher's Edition 436A).

Clements, D., and M. Batista. "Learning of Geometric Concepts in a Logo Environment." *Journal for Research in Mathematics Education,* 20 (1989), pp. 450–467. (See Teacher's Edition p. 316A)

Cognition and Technology Group at Vanderbilt. "Looking at Technology in Context: A framework for understanding technology and education research." *The Handbook of Educational Psychology,* DC Berliner & RC Calfee, eds. NY: Macmillan. (1996), pp. 807–840. (See Teacher's Edition page T38.)

Cotton, K. "Monitoring Student Learning in the Classroom." Portland, OR *Northwest Regional Educational Laboratory.* (2001) (See pages T15, T16 and T21.)

Cuevas, G. J, P. H. Mann, and R. M. McClung. "The Effects of a Language Process Approach Program on the Mathematics Achievements of First, Third, and Fifth Graders." *Paper presented at the meeting of the American Educational Research Association,* San Francisco, CA (1986), (See Teacher's Edition page T21.)

Diezmann and English. "The Roles of Representation in School Mathematics." Virginia: NCTM. (2001), p. 88. (See Teacher's Edition page T19.)

Dreher, M. J. "Fostering Reading for Learning." In L. Baker, M. J. Dreher, & J. T. Guthrie (Eds.), *Engaging Young Readers: Promoting achievement and motivation* (2000), pp. 68–93. (See Teacher's Edition page T34.)

Empson, Susan B. "Low-Performing Students and Teaching Fractions for Understanding: An Interactional Analysis." *Journal for Research in Mathematics Education* 34 (4) (2003), pp. 305–343. (See Teacher's Edition page T14.)

Engelhardt, J. M., and V. Usnick. "When Should We Teach Regrouping in Addition and Subtraction." *School Science and Mathematics,* 91 (1) (1991) PP. 6–9. (See Teacher's Edition p. 94A)

Fillmore, L. W, and L. M. Meyer. "The Curriculum and Linguistic Minorities." In P. W. Jackson (Ed.), *Handbook of Research on Curriculum:* (1996), pp. 626–658. (See Teacher's Edition page T24.)

Hiebert, J., and D. Wearne. "Procedures Over Concepts: The Acquisition of Decimal Number Knowledge." In Conceptual and Procedural Knowledge: The Case of Mathematics. Edited by J. Hiebert. Mahwah, NJ: Lawrence Erlbaum, 1986. (See Teachers Edition pp. 338A)

Hiebert, J, and M. M. Lindquist. "Developing Mathematical Knowledge in the Young Child." In J. Payne (Ed.) *Mathematic for the Young Child* Reston, VA NCTM (1990), pp. 17–36. (See Teacher's Edition page T18.)

These research documents are referenced in "Research says …" statements on pp. T14–T38 in this book and in "Research says …" statements in the Math Background for Teachers within lessons.

Hong, H. "Effects of Mathematics Learning through Children's Literature on Math Achievement and Dispositional Outcomes." *Early Childhood Research Quarterly* 11 (4) (1996), pp. 477–494. (See Teacher's Edition page T32.)

Jones, G. A., C. W. Langrall, C. A. Thornton, A. T. Mogill. "Students' Probabilistic Thinking in Instruction." *Journal for Research in Mathematics Education*, 30 (1999), pp, 487–519. (See Teacher's Edition p. 440A)

Kouba, V. L., and K. Franklin. "Multiplication and Division: Sense Making and Meaning." In *Research Ideas for the Classroom: Early Childhood Mathematics*. Edited by R. Jensen. New York: Macmillan Publishing Company, 1993. (See Teacher's Edition pp. 182A, 206A)

Lampert, M. "Knowing, Doing, and Teaching Multiplication." *Cognition and Instruction* 3 (1986), pp. 305–342. (See Teacher's Edition page T17.)

Mack, N. K. "Learning Fractions with Understanding: Building on Informal Knowledge." *Journal for Research in Mathematics Education* 21 (1990), pp. 16–32. (See Teacher's Edition page T17.)

Mathematics Learning Study Committee. *Adding It Up: Helping Children Learn Mathematics*. Edited by J. Kilpatrick, J. Swafford, and B. Findell. Washington, D.C.: National Academy Press, 2001. (See Teacher's Edition pp. 56A, 138A, 186A)

Mayer, R. E. "Models for Understanding." *Review of Research in Education*, 59 (1989), pp. 43–64. (Teacher's Edition page T18.)

Mayer, R. E. and M.C. Wittrock. "Problem-Solving Transfer." In D. C. Berliner and R. C. Calfee (Eds.), *Handbook of Educational Psychology* (1996), pp. 47–62. (See Teacher's Edition page T26.)

Mulligan, J. T., and M. C. Mitchelmore. "Young Children's Intuitive Models of Multiplication and Division." *Journal for Research in Mathematics Education*, 28 (3) (1997), pp. 309–330. (See Teacher's Edition pp. 116A, 212A, 222A)

Nesher, P. "Multiplicative School Word Problems: Theoretical approaches and empirical findings." In J. Hiebert & M. Behr (Eds.) *Number Concepts and Operations in the Middle Grades* Reston, VA: NCTM. (1988), pp. 162–181. (See Teacher's Edition page T28.)

Paris, S. G. & Cunningham, A. E. "Children becoming students." In D. C. Berliner & R. C. Calfee (Eds.), *Handbook of Educational Psychology* (1996), pp. 117–147. (See Teacher's Edition page T30.)

Pesek, Dolores D, and David Kirshner. "Interference of Instrumental Instruction in Subsequent Relational Learning." *Journal for Research in Mathematics Education* 31 (5) (2000), pp. 524–540. (See Teacher's Edition page T16.)

Pike, C. L. "The Use of Symbols, Words, and Diagrams as Indicators of Mathematical Cognition: A causal model." *Journal for Research in Mathematics Education*, 34 (2003), pp. 406–432. (See Teacher's Edition page T31.)

Reys, B. J., and R. E. Reys. "Estimation-Directions from the Standards." *Arithmetic Teacher*, 37 (7) (1990), pp. 22–25. (See Teacher's Edition p. 80A)

Richards, D. D., and R. S. Siegler. "The Development of Time, Speed, and Distance Concepts." Paper presented at the Biennial Meeting of the Society for Research in Child Development (San Francisco, California, March 15–18, 1979). (See Teacher's Edition p. 414A)

Rightsel, P.S., and C.A. Thornton. "72 Addition Facts Can Be Mastered by Mid-Grade 1." *Arithmetic Teacher*, 33 (3) (1985), pp 8–10. (See Teachers Edition p. 284A)

Schwartz, D. L. & Heiser, J. "Spatial Representations and Imagery in Learning." In R. K. Sawyer (Ed.), *The Cambridge Handbook of the Learning Sciences* (2006), pp. 283–298. (See Teacher's Edition page T18.)

Schwartz, DL, X. Lin, S. Brophy, and JC Bransford. "Toward the Development of Flexibly Adaptive Instructional Designs." *Instructional Design Theories and Models*. CM Reigelut, ed. Hillsdale, NJ: Erlbaum. II (1999), pp. 183–213. (See Teacher's Edition page T22.)

Shavelson, R. J. "Review of Research on Teachers' Pedagogical Judgments, Plans, and Decisions." *The Elementary School Journal* 83 (1983), pp. 392–413. (See Teacher's Edition page T15.)

Smith, S. S. *Early Childhood Mathematics*. Boston; Allyn and Bacon, 2001. (See Teacher's Edition p. 158A)

Vye, NJ, DL Schwartz, JD Bransford, BJ Barron, L. Zech, and Cognition and Technology Group at Vanderbilt. " SMART Environments That Support Monitoring, Reflection, and Revision." Metacognition in Educational Theory and Practice. D. Hacker, J. Dunlosky, and A. Graessner, eds. Mahwah, NJ: Erlbaum (1998) (See Teacher's Edition page T20.)

Wilson, P., and A. Osborne. "Foundational Ideas in Teaching About Measurement." In *Teaching Mathematics in Grades K–8: Research Based Methods*. Edited by T. Post. Boston: Allyn and Bacon, 1988. (See Teacher's Edition p. 380A)

Wilson, P., and R. Rowland. "Teaching Measurement." In *Research Ideas for the Classroom: Early Childhood Mathematics*. Edited by R. Jensen. New York: Macmillan, 1993. (See Teacher's Edition p. 396A)

enVisionMATH Illinois

Problem Solving Using
Number and Operations

Superman's Town

Metropolis is the name of the make-believe town where Superman lives. Metropolis is also a real town in Illinois, and it has a 15-foot statue of Superman. The town's Superman Museum has costumes and items used in Superman movies. Metropolis has a Superman festival every year.

Largest *Tyrannosaurus rex*

Sue is the largest, most complete *Tyrannosaurus rex* fossil ever found. The fossil is 42 feet long. Sue's 58 teeth show *T. rex* was a meat eater. The longest teeth are 12 inches long. About $\frac{2}{3}$ of each tooth is inside the jawbone. Only $\frac{1}{3}$ of each tooth stuck out of Sue's gums. Sue is at the Field Museum in Chicago.

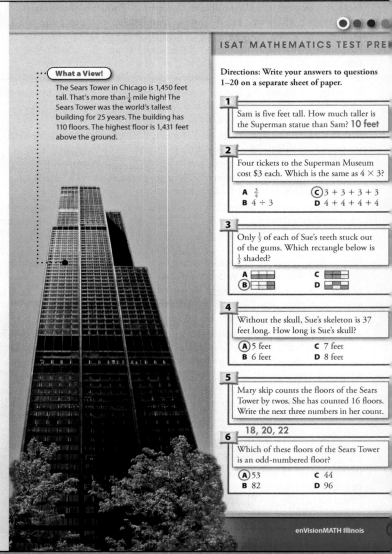

What a View!

The Sears Tower in Chicago is 1,450 feet tall. That's more than $\frac{1}{4}$ mile high! The Sears Tower was the world's tallest building for 25 years. The building has 110 floors. The highest floor is 1,431 feet above the ground.

Directions: Write your answers to questions 1–20 on a separate sheet of paper.

1 Sam is five feet tall. How much taller is the Superman statue than Sam? **10 feet**

2 Four tickets to the Superman Museum cost $3 each. Which is the same as 4×3?

A $\frac{4}{4}$ (C) $3 + 3 + 3 + 3$
B $4 \div 3$ D $4 + 4 + 4 + 4$

3 Only $\frac{1}{3}$ of each of Sue's teeth stuck out of the gums. Which rectangle below is $\frac{1}{3}$ shaded?

A   C
(B)   D

4 Without the skull, Sue's skeleton is 37 feet long. How long is Sue's skull?

(A) 5 feet C 7 feet
B 6 feet D 8 feet

5 Mary skip counts the floors of the Sears Tower by twos. She has counted 16 floors. Write the next three numbers in her count.

18, 20, 22

6 Which of these floors of the Sears Tower is an odd-numbered floor?

(A) 53 C 44
B 82 D 96

x

Number and Operations

Purpose
Provide practice using Illinois data and review math skills from previous Illinois Mathematics Assessment Framework Objectives and the Illinois Mathematics Performance Descriptors.

Exercise 1 Ask students to find the height of the Superman Statue in the caption. Students can then solve the number sentence $15 - 5 = 10$.

Exercise 2 Review the relationship between addition and multiplication. Multiplication involves the joining of equal groups. In this case, there are four groups of three.

Exercise 3 Remind students the set of six rectangles represents a whole. The shaded rectangles are a subset of the whole. $\frac{1}{3}$ of 6 is 2, so two rectangles should be shaded.

Exercise 4 Remind students to use information contained in both the caption and question. Using these sources, students can write and solve the number sentence $42 - 37 = 5$.

Exercise 5 Point out students can use the strategy of counting on from 16 to check their answers. Every second number is part of the count.

Exercise 6 Point out students can identify even numbers by skip counting by 2 from a number whose ones digit is 0. Even numbers end in 0, 2, 4, 6, or 8. Odd numbers end in 1, 3, 5, 7, or 9.

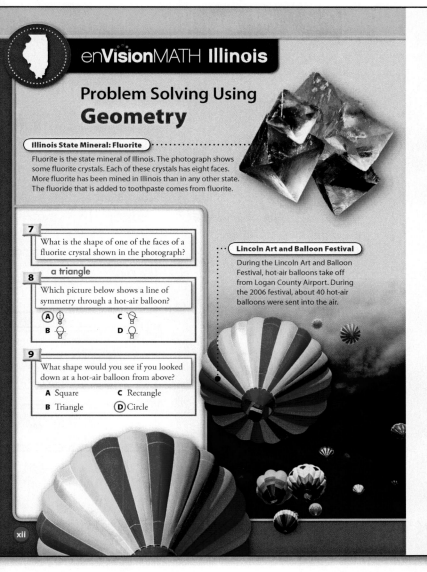

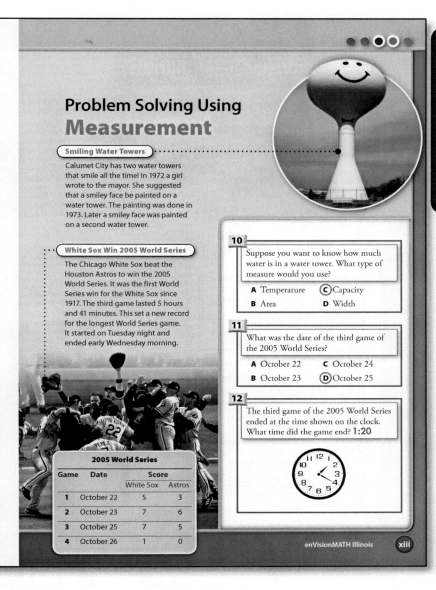

enVisionMATH Illinois

Problem Solving Using
Geometry

Illinois State Mineral: Fluorite

Fluorite is the state mineral of Illinois. The photograph shows some fluorite crystals. Each of these crystals has eight faces. More fluorite has been mined in Illinois than in any other state. The fluoride that is added to toothpaste comes from fluorite.

7

What is the shape of one of the faces of a fluorite crystal shown in the photograph?

a triangle

8

Which picture below shows a line of symmetry through a hot-air balloon?

(A)   **C**

B   **D**

9

What shape would you see if you looked down at a hot-air balloon from above?

A Square   C Rectangle
B Triangle   **(D)** Circle

Lincoln Art and Balloon Festival

During the Lincoln Art and Balloon Festival, hot-air balloons take off from Logan County Airport. During the 2006 festival, about 40 hot-air balloons were sent into the air.

xii

Problem Solving Using
Measurement

Smiling Water Towers

Calumet City has two water towers that smile all the time! In 1972 a girl wrote to the mayor. She suggested that a smiley face be painted on a water tower. The painting was done in 1973. Later a smiley face was painted on a second water tower.

White Sox Win 2005 World Series

The Chicago White Sox beat the Houston Astros to win the 2005 World Series. It was the first World Series win for the White Sox since 1917. The third game lasted 5 hours and 41 minutes. This set a new record for the longest World Series game. It started on Tuesday night and ended early Wednesday morning.

10

Suppose you want to know how much water is in a water tower. What type of measure would you use?

A Temperature   **(C)** Capacity
B Area   D Width

11

What was the date of the third game of the 2005 World Series?

A October 22   C October 24
B October 23   **(D)** October 25

12

The third game of the 2005 World Series ended at the time shown on the clock. What time did the game end? **1:20**

2005 World Series			
Game	Date	Score	
		White Sox	Astros
1	October 22	5	3
2	October 23	7	6
3	October 25	7	5
4	October 26	1	0

 **Geometry**

Exercise 7 Ask students to count the edges of a crystal face in the photograph. Ask students what shape has three sides.

Exercise 8 Students may forget that a line of symmetry must do more than divide an object in two parts. Point out that the two parts need to be mirror images.

Exercise 9 Suggest that students put their fingertips together as if they were reaching around the widest part of a hot-air balloon. Ask what shape their hands form.

Measurement

Exercise 10 Point out that the measure needs to account for three dimensions. Remind students that the amount of liquid a container can hold when it is full is called its capacity.

Exercise 11 Students may have picked the third answer choice as the date of the third game. Point out that the table shows a one-day break between the second and third games.

Exercise 12 The numbers on a clock may confuse students when they are reading minutes. Have them multiply the last number the minute hand has passed by five, then add the number of marks the minute hand has passed after that number.

Other Illinois Features
- The **Illinois Teacher's Edition** for each topic contains a correlation of that topic's lessons to the Illinois Mathematics Assessment Framework Objectives and the Illinois Mathematics Performance Descriptors.
- In the **Illinois Overview Teacher's Edition**, Topic Planner pages correlate each topic's lessons to the Illinois

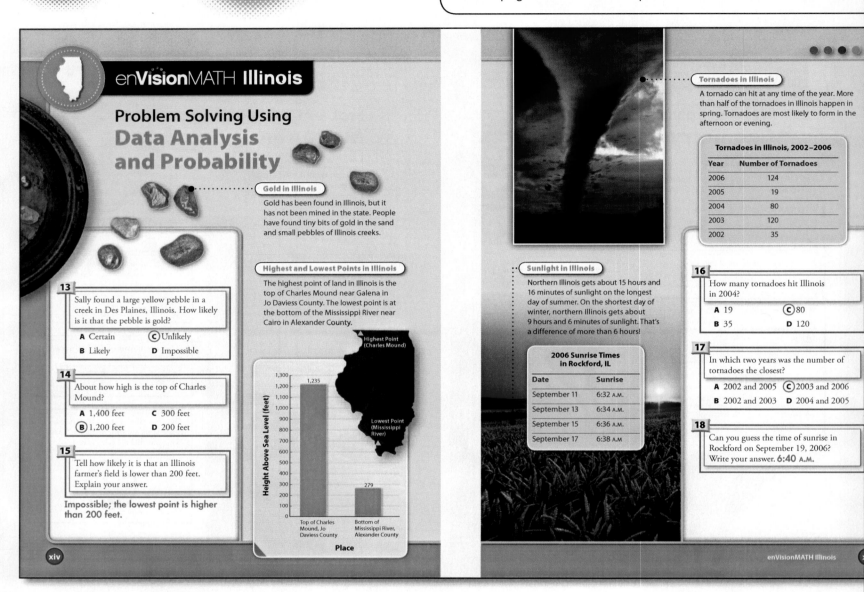

enVisionMATH Illinois

Problem Solving Using
Data Analysis and Probability

Gold in Illinois

Gold has been found in Illinois, but it has not been mined in the state. People have found tiny bits of gold in the sand and small pebbles of Illinois creeks.

13 Sally found a large yellow pebble in a creek in Des Plaines, Illinois. How likely is it that the pebble is gold?

A Certain   **C** Unlikely
B Likely   **D** Impossible

14 About how high is the top of Charles Mound?

A 1,400 feet   **C** 300 feet
B 1,200 feet   **D** 200 feet

15 Tell how likely it is that an Illinois farmer's field is lower than 200 feet. Explain your answer.

Impossible; the lowest point is higher than 200 feet.

Highest and Lowest Points in Illinois

The highest point of land in Illinois is the top of Charles Mound near Galena in Jo Daviess County. The lowest point is at the bottom of the Mississippi River near Cairo in Alexander County.

Highest Point (Charles Mound)

Lowest Point (Mississippi River)

Chart: Height Above Sea Level (feet) — Top of Charles Mound, Jo Daviess County: 1,235; Bottom of Mississippi River, Alexander County: 279. **Place**

Sunlight in Illinois

Northern Illinois gets about 15 hours and 16 minutes of sunlight on the longest day of summer. On the shortest day of winter, northern Illinois gets about 9 hours and 6 minutes of sunlight. That's a difference of more than 6 hours!

2006 Sunrise Times in Rockford, IL

Date	Sunrise
September 11	6:32 A.M.
September 13	6:34 A.M.
September 15	6:36 A.M.
September 17	6:38 A.M

Tornadoes in Illinois

A tornado can hit at any time of the year. More than half of the tornadoes in Illinois happen in spring. Tornadoes are most likely to form in the afternoon or evening.

Tornadoes in Illinois, 2002–2006

Year	Number of Tornadoes
2006	124
2005	19
2004	80
2003	120
2002	35

16 How many tornadoes hit Illinois in 2004?

A 19   **C** 80
B 35   **D** 120

17 In which two years was the number of tornadoes the closest?

A 2002 and 2005   **C** 2003 and 2006
B 2002 and 2003   **D** 2004 and 2005

18 Can you guess the time of sunrise in Rockford on September 19, 2006? Write your answer. 6:40 A.M.

Data Analysis and Probability

Exercise 13 Point out that the caption describes "tiny bits" of gold being found in Illinois creeks. The chance of finding a large pebble is unlikely but not impossible.

Exercises 14 and 15 Students may need help reading the graph's vertical axis. Point out that the top of the higher bar is closest to the line extending horizontally from 1,200. Point out that the top of the lower bar reaches above the line extending horizontally from 200.

Exercises 16 and 17 Have students describe the table aloud. Verbalizing may aid understanding of the data presented in the table.

Exercise 18 Students may not notice the dates in the table advance by two days and the times become later by two minutes. Point out these patterns.

Mathematics Assessment Framework Objectives and the Illinois Mathematics Performance Descriptors. A full correlation to the Illinois Mathematics Assessment Framework Objectives and the Illinois Mathematics Performance Descriptors is also provided.

- The **Illinois Overview Teacher's Edition** also contains Pacing for Test Success pages that provide instruction on content before taking the ISAT Mathematics Test.

- For test preparation use the **ISAT Mathematics Test Prep** workbook.
- The **Illinois Math Diagnosis and Intervention System (MDIS)** correlates Intervention Lessons and Diagnostic Tests to the Illinois Mathematics Assessment Framework Objectives and the Illinois Mathematics Performance Descriptors.
- Illinois technology products include state-specific versions of the **Online Lesson Planner, ExamView,** and **SuccessTracker.**

Item Analysis for Diagnosis and Intervention

IL Grade 2 Math Assessment Framework Objectives	Descriptor Identifiers	Items	MDIS Lessons
6.2.09 Solve problems and number sentences involving addition and subtraction with and without regrouping.	6B.Stage B.5	1, 4	B42, C29
6.2.04 Represent multiplication as repeated addition.	6B.Stage B.4	2	B43, B50
6.2.03 Recognize fractions represented with a pictorial model.	6B.Stage B.4	3	A44, A48, A49
8.2.01 Determine a missing term in a pattern, describe a pattern, and extend a pattern when given a pattern.	6A.Stage B.1	5	A74, A75
6.2.08 Solve problems involving descriptions of numbers, including characteristics and relationships.	6A.Stage B.5	6	A74, A75
9.2.07 Recognize the two-dimensional components of a three-dimensional object.	9B.Stage B.2	7, 9	D59, D64
9.2.04 Identify whether a figure has a line of symmetry, and sketch or identify the line of symmetry.	9A.Stage B.4	8	D67
7.5.02 (Preview) Select and use appropriate standard units and tools to measure length, mass/weight, capacity, and angles.	7A.Stage B.1	10	D40
10.2.01 Read and interpret data represented in a pictograph, bar graph, tally chart, or table.	7A.Stage B.3	11	E29
7.2.02 Select and use appropriate standard units and tools to measure length, time, and temperature.	7A.Stage B.4	12	D14
10.2.04 Classify events using words such as likely, maybe, and not likely.	10C.Stage B.1	13, 15	D86
10.2.01 Read and interpret data represented in a pictograph, bar graph, tally chart, or table.	10A.Stage B.1	14, 16, 17	D83, D84, E29
10.2.02 Complete missing parts of a pictograph, bar graph, tally chart, or table for a given set of data.	10A.Stage B.2	18	E29, A76
8.2.01 Determine a missing term in a pattern, describe a pattern, and extend a pattern when given a pattern.	8D.Stage B.1	19, 20	A74, A75

Algebra

Exercise 19 Have students locate the numbers 210, 240, 270, and 300 on a number line. Ask them to find the pattern in the numbers and then to use the pattern to find the next number.

Exercise 20 Ask students to extend the number pattern to zero. Then ask them to count the number of times they needed to use the pattern. Describe how the pattern shows the miles left at the end of each day.

Content Focus and Coherence

Big Ideas		Content Strands					
		1	2	3	4	5	6
		Number and Operations	Algebra	Geometry	Measurement	Data Analysis and Probability	Problem Solving
1	**Number Uses, Classification, and Representation** Numbers can be used for different purposes, and numbers can be classified and represented in different ways.	■	■				
2	**Numbers and the Number Line** The set of real numbers is infinite and ordered. Whole numbers, integers, and fractions are real numbers. Each real number can be associated with a unique point on the number line.	■					
3	**The Base-Ten Numeration System** The base-ten numeration system is a scheme for recording numbers using digits 0–9, groups of ten, and place value.	■					
4	**Equivalence** Any number, measure, numerical expression, algebraic expression, or equation can be represented in an infinite number of ways that have the same value.	■		■			
5	**Comparison and Relationships** Numbers, expressions, measures, and objects can be compared and related to other numbers, expressions, measures, and objects in different ways.	■		■	■		
6	**Operation Meanings and Relationships** There are multiple interpretations of addition, subtraction, multiplication, and division of rational numbers, and each operation is related to other operations.	■					
7	**Properties** For a given set of numbers there are relationships that are always true, called properties, and these are the rules that govern arithmetic and algebra.	■	■				
8	**Basic Facts and Algorithms** There is more than one algorithm for each of the operations with rational numbers. Some strategies for basic facts and most algorithms for operations with rational numbers, both mental math and paper and pencil, use equivalence to transform calculations into simpler ones.	■	■				
9	**Estimation** Numbers can be approximated by numbers that are close. Numerical calculations can be approximated by replacing numbers with other numbers that are close and easy to compute with mentally. Some measurements can be approximated using known referents as the unit in the measurement process.	■			■		
10	**Ratio and Proportionality** When mathematical or real-world quantities have a relationship that can be stated as "for every x units of the first quantity there are y units of the second quantity," this relationship can be described using a ratio. Proportionality involves a relationship in which the ratio of two quantities remains constant as the corresponding values of the quantities change. In a proportional relationship there are an infinite number of ratios equal to the lowest terms or constant ratio.	■		■	■	■	
11	**Patterns, Relations, and Functions** Relationships can be described and generalizations made for mathematical situations that have numbers or objects that repeat in predictable ways. For some relationships, mathematical expressions and equations can be used to describe how members of one set are related to members of a second set.	■	■	■		■	
12	**Solving Equations and Inequalities** Rules of arithmetic and algebra can be used together with notions of equivalence to transform equations and inequalities so solutions can be found.		■				
13	**Variable** Mathematical situations and structures can be translated and represented abstractly using variables, expressions, and equations.		■				
14	**Geometric Figures** Two- and three-dimensional objects with or without curved surfaces can be described, classified, and analyzed by their attributes. An object's location in space can be described quantitatively.			■	■		
15	**Transformations** Objects in space can be transformed in an infinite number of ways, and those transformations can be described and analyzed mathematically.			■			
16	**Measurement** Some attributes of objects are measurable and can be quantified using unit amounts.				■		
17	**Data Collection and Representation** Some questions can be answered by collecting and analyzing data, and the question to be answered determines the data that needs to be collected and how best to collect it. Data can be represented visually using tables, charts, and graphs. The type of data determines the best choice of visual representation.					■	
18	**Data Distribution** There are special numerical measures that describe the center and spread of numerical data sets. The most appropriate measures for a situation depend on the nature of the data and on the use to be made of the measures.					■	
19	**Chance** The chance of an event occurring can be described numerically by a number between 0 and 1 inclusive and used to make predictions about other events.					■	
20	**Mathematical Processes** Doing mathematics involves a variety of processes including problem solving, reasoning, communicating, connecting, and representing.						■

Grade K Topics	Grade 1 Topics	Grade 2 Topics	Grade 3 Topics	Grade 4 Topics	Grade 5 Topics	Grade 6 Topics
4, 5, 8, 12	1, 5, 10, 11	4, 17	1	1, 8, 10	1, 3, 4, 9, 10	1, 5, 7
5, 8	19	12	12, 13	10, 12	9, 17	5, 6, 10
2	10, 11, 12	4, 17	1, 13	1, 12	1	1
4, 5, 13	5, 11	5	1, 2, 6, 8, 12	2, 5, 10	3, 4, 9, 16	1, 3, 5, 6, 14
2, 4, 6, 9, 13, 14, 15, 16	1, 2, 6, 7, 12, 14	2, 3, 4, 17	1, 12	1, 10, 12	1, 9	1, 10, 12
10, 11	3, 4, 5, 7, 17	1, 3, 9, 19, 20	2, 3, 5, 7, 8	3, 4, 8	11	8, 9
	3, 16	2, 8, 19	2, 5, 6, 8	3, 4	3, 6	2, 4
	6, 16, 20	2, 6, 7, 8, 9, 10, 17, 18	2, 3, 4, 6, 12, 13, 18, 19	2, 3, 5, 7, 8, 11, 13	2, 3, 4, 5, 7, 10, 11	2, 3, 7, 8, 9
	12	10, 12, 13, 14, 18	2, 3, 12, 16, 18, 19	1, 2, 5, 7, 8, 10, 13, 14, 16	2, 3, 4, 5, 7, 12, 13	3, 7, 8, 9, 14, 15
3, 12	1, 9, 10	4, 6, 7, 17	1, 2, 3, 5, 9, 18, 19	3, 5, 6, 7, 8, 14, 20	2, 3, 4, 5, 7, 8, 15	1, 2, 5, 6, 15, 18, 19, 20
			9	6, 18	6	2
				16	14, 16	12, 13, 14, 15, 16, 17
			3, 4, 6, 18	2, 8, 13, 14, 18	15	1, 3, 4, 7, 10, 14, 15
7	8, 18	11, 16	10, 20	9, 15, 17	8, 13, 17	10, 11, 18
7	8	11	11	19	19	11
9, 13, 14, 15	13, 14, 15	5, 13, 14, 15	14, 15, 16, 17	9, 14, 16	12, 13, 14	16, 17, 18
6	18	16	20	17	17, 18	19
				17	18	19
6	18	16	20	20	20	20
1–16	1–20	1–20	1–20	1–20	1–20	1–20

Big Ideas are the conceptual underpinnings of the program. They are the glue that provide conceptual cohesion across lessons, topics, and grades.
Essential Understandings are specific ideas that contribute to the Big Idea. Big Ideas connect Essential Understandings that occur within and across lessons. Math Background for Teachers in each topic shows the Big Ideas and Essential Understandings for the topic.

Organization of the Content

Program

> **❶** Content Strands and Big Ideas

Grade

> **❶** Mathematics Performance Descriptors, Assessment Framework Objectives, and NCTM Curriculum Focal Points/Connections*

Lesson

> Lesson Objectives and Essential Understandings

*See the Grade 3 NCTM Curriculum Focal Points/ Connections correlation beginning on p. T170.

Pacing for Test Success in **Illinois**

Get ready for the ISAT!

Teach all Grade 3 tested content before the ISAT by using Pacing for Test Success!

What is Pacing for Test Success in Illinois?

Pacing for Test Success in Illinois is a plan for successfully addressing all the Grade 3 content that is assessed on the ISAT before the ISAT is given. It provides 100 daily, short activities created from lessons towards the end of the student book. Each activity relates to geometry, measurement, algebra, data analysis, or probability. Use the Pacing for Test Success activities in conjunction with student book lessons that focus on content assessed on the ISAT to make sure students have experience with all the assessed content prior to taking the ISAT.

How to Use Pacing for Test Success in Illinois?

These 5-10 minute activities can be used at the start of class or anytime during the day. The information in the chart at the right includes:

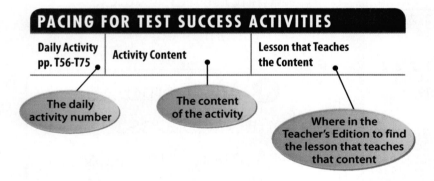

PACING FOR TEST SUCCESS ACTIVITIES

Daily Activity pp. T56-T75	Activity Content	Lesson that Teaches the Content

The daily activity number

The content of the activity

Where in the Teacher's Edition to find the lesson that teaches that content

If the ISAT assesses lessons that you don't think you'll get to before the test, then use as many of the Pacing for Test Success Activities as needed in order to teach the content of those lessons before the test.

PACING FOR TEST SUCCESS ACTIVITIES

Daily Activity pp. T56-T75	Activity Content	Lesson that Teaches the Content
1	Build a prism	Lesson 15-4
2	Volume of a cube	Lesson 15-4
3	Dimension change	Lesson 15-4
4	Start the pattern	Lesson 15-5
5	Missing pattern parts	Lesson 15-5
6	Nonstandard units	Lesson 16-1
7	Customary units of length	Lesson 16-1
8	Comparing lengths	Lesson 16-1
9	Choosing units of capacity	Lesson 16-2
10	Comparing units of capacity	Lesson 16-2
11	Pounds and ounces	Lesson 16-3
12	Estimate the weight	Lesson 16-3
13	Changing metric units of length	Lesson 16-4
14	What's my weight?	Lesson 16-4
15	Find a rule	Lesson 16-4
16	Millimeters and centimeters	Lesson 16-5
17	Meters and kilometers	Lesson 16-5
18	Draw and order	Lesson 16-5
19	Milliliters and liters	Lesson 16-6
20	Name the item	Lesson 16-6
21	Grams and kilograms	Lesson 16-7
22	Compare to a kilogram	Lesson 16-7
23	Changing from larger units to smaller units	Lesson 16-8
24	Changing from smaller units to larger units	Lesson 16-8
25	Equivalent metric measurements	Lesson 16-8
26	Units of time	Lesson 16-9
27	Changing units of time	Lesson 16-9
28	Compare times	Lesson 16-9
29	Elapsed time	Lesson 16-10
30	Using elapsed time	Lesson 16-10
31	Temperature scales	Lesson 16-11
32	Temperature changes	Lesson 16-11
33	More about temperature changes	Lesson 16-11

Daily Activity pp. T56-T75	Activity Content	Lesson that Teaches the Content
34	Work backward	Lesson 16-12
35	More about working backward	Lesson 16-12
36	Survey questions	Lesson 17-1
37	Conduct a survey	Lesson 17-1
38	Data from surveys	Lesson 17-1
39	Reading bar graphs	Lesson 17-2
40	Interpreting bar graphs	Lesson 17-2
41	Make a line plot	Lesson 17-3
42	Read a line plot	Lesson 17-3
43	Write the ordered pair	Lesson 17-4
44	Name the point	Lesson 17-4
45	More about ordered pairs	Lesson 17-4
46	Read line graphs	Lesson 17-5
47	Interpret a line graph	Lesson 17-5
48	Finding the mean	Lesson 17-6
49	More about finding the mean	Lesson 17-6
50	Finding sets of numbers	Lesson 17-6
51	Median	Lesson 17-7
52	Mode	Lesson 17-7
53	Range	Lesson 17-7
54	Understand stem-and-leaf plots	Lesson 17-8
55	Median, mode, and range	Lesson 17-8
56	Read a circle graph	Lesson 17-9
57	Interpret a circle graph	Lesson 17-9
58	Completing a bar graph	Lesson 17-10
59	Making a bar graph	Lesson 17-10
60	More about making a bar graph	Lesson 17-10
61	Balanced equations	Lesson 18-1
62	True or false?	Lesson 18-1
63	Is it true?	Lesson 18-1
64	Using addition and subtraction to solve	Lesson 18-2
65	Solving equations	Lesson 18-2
66	True or false?	Lesson 18-3
67	Identify the inverse operation	Lesson 18-3
68	Solving equations	Lesson 18-3

PACING FOR TEST SUCCESS ACTIVITIES

Daily Activity pp. T56-T75	Activity Content	Lesson that Teaches the Content
69	Inequalities	Lesson 18-4
70	Graphing inequalities on a number line	Lesson 18-4
71	Work backward	Lesson 18-5
72	Work backward from a given time	Lesson 18-5
73	Translations	Lesson 19-1
74	Two-step translations	Lesson 19-1
75	Find the translations	Lesson 19-1
76	Identify the reflection	Lesson 19-2
77	Letter reflections	Lesson 19-2
78	Two-step reflections	Lesson 19-2
79	Rotations	Lesson 19-3
80	Draw and rotate	Lesson 19-3
81	Same shape and size	Lesson 19-4
82	Draw a congruent figure	Lesson 19-4
83	More congruent figures	Lesson 19-4
84	Lines of symmetry	Lesson 19-5
85	Symmetric drawings	Lesson 19-5
86	Rotational symmetry	Lesson 19-6
87	Quadrilaterals and rotational symmetry	Lesson 19-6
88	Letters and rotational symmetry	Lesson 19-6
89	Draw a picture	Lesson 19-7
90	More drawing a picture	Lesson 19-7
91	Use objects for combinations	Lesson 20-1
92	Use pictures for combinations	Lesson 20-1
93	Outcomes and tree diagrams	Lesson 20-2
94	Multiply to find outcomes	Lesson 20-2
95	Possible outcomes	Lesson 20-2
96	Describing events	Lesson 20-3
97	Fractions for probability	Lesson 20-3
98	More fractions for probability	Lesson 20-3
99	Use tables to reason	Lesson 20-4
100	Use reasoning and tables	Lesson 20-4

PACING FOR TEST SUCCESS

Trapezoids and parallelograms

- Draw a trapezoid on the board. Write the word *trapezoid* and define it. (See page 250.) Then draw and label a parallelogram. Say, *A parallelogram has two pairs of parallel sides.*

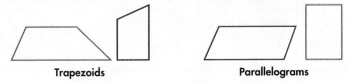

Trapezoids   **Parallelograms**

- Then ask, *Is a parallelogram a trapezoid?* (No)
- Ask, *How are these figures alike? How are they different?* (They are both quadrilaterals; the parallelogram has two pairs of sides parallel, the trapezoid has one pair of sides parallel.)

Kinds of parallelograms

- Draw and label a parallelogram and a rectangle. Remind students that a rectangle is a parallelogram with four right angles.
- Ask, *How are these figures alike? How are they different?*
- Ask, *Are all parallelograms also rectangles?* (No) *Are all rectangles also parallelograms?* (Yes)
- Have students draw two examples of each figure.

Square and rhombus

- Draw and define a square and a rhombus. (See page 251.)
- Ask, *How are these figures alike? How are they different? Are they quadrilaterals?* (Yes) *trapezoids?* (No) *parallelograms?* (Yes) *rectangles?* (The square is; the rhombus is not.)
- Have students provide clues about a figure while classmates guess what the figure is.

Generalizations

- Tell students *A statement is true only if it is <u>always</u> true. To test a statement, ask, "Can I find or draw an exception?"*
- Provide some general statements and ask students if they are true.
  An odd number is never even.
  When it rains, the ground gets wet.
  When the ground is wet, it is raining.
  Polygons have straight sides.

More about generalizations

- Explain how certain words like *some, all, never, no,* and *always* can change a true statement to a false statement, or vice versa. Ask students to list other similar words that do the same thing.

- Give the statements, *Rectangles are squares* and *Some rectangles are squares.*
- Provide some general statements and ask students to insert a word that makes each statement true.
  Multiples of 5 are ____ odd numbers. (sometimes)
  ____ trapezoids are squares. (No)
  ____ squares are quadrilaterals. (All)
- Invite students to write and exchange statements of their own.

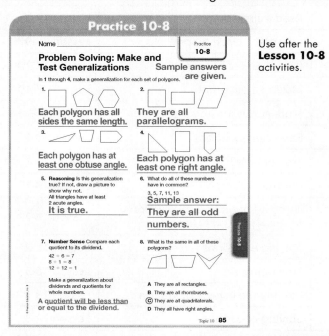

Use after the **Lesson 10-7** activities.

Use after the **Lesson 10-8** activities.

Activity 6 (Lesson 11-1)

Congruent figures

- Write the word "congruent" on the board. Fold or cut two pieces of paper to create two polygons that are the same size and shape. Show students that they fit exactly on top of one another and explain that the polygons are congruent. (See page 260.)
- Repeat with other congruent polygons. Ask, *When are two figures congruent?* (They are the same size and shape.) *Can a triangle and a square be congruent?* (No, they are different shapes.)
- Ask students to identify congruent figures in the classroom.

Activity 7 (Lesson 11-1)

Slides and turns

- Write "slide" and "translation" on the board. Have students trace a polygon, slide it and trace it again. Ask, *Are the two polygons congruent?* (Yes, they are the same size and shape.)
- Demonstrate how to rotate a figure about a point while students rotate their figures. *Does a turn, or rotation, also give congruent figures?* (Yes, neither the shape nor its size changes.)

Activity 8 (Lesson 11-1)

Flips

- Provide each student with a polygon shape cut from an index card. Ask each student to trace the polygon on paper, flip it, and then trace the resulting mirror image of the polygon.
- Ask, *How do you know that the first and second polygons are congruent?* (They are the same size and shape.) Say: *The mirror image of a figure is called its reflection.* Have students repeat this with two other polygons.
- Play a game in which you draw pairs of figures on the board and ask students to decide if they show slides, turns, or flips.

Activity 9 (Lesson 11-2)

Symmetric figures

- Using Teaching Tool 38, cut out several polygons. Fold a rectangle in half to show that two sides match. Introduce the terms "symmetric" and "line of symmetry." (See page 264.)

- Show other polygons and ask students to help you identify which are symmetric. For each figure that is symmetric, identify the line of symmetry.

Activity 10 (Lesson 11-2)

Line of symmetry

- Draw a square on the board. Ask, *How many lines of symmetry does a square have?* (4) Repeat with an equilateral triangle, pentagon, and rectangle. Explain that some symmetrical figures may have more than one line of symmetry.

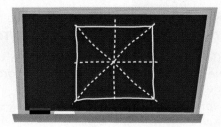

- Provide pairs of students with a copy of Teaching Tool 38 and have them cut out the polygons. Ask students to determine how many lines of symmetry their shapes have. Sort the shapes by the number of lines of symmetry.

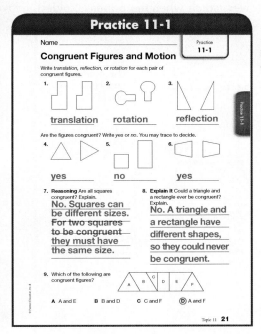

Use after the **Lesson 11-1** activities.

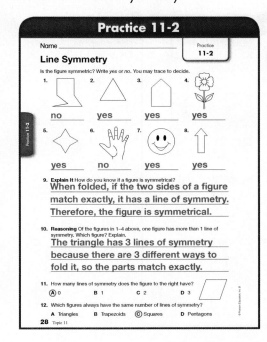

Use after the **Lesson 11-2** activities.

PACING FOR TEST SUCCESS

Activity 11 (Lesson 11-3)

Drawing shapes with lines of symmetry

- Use Dot Paper (Teaching Tool 17) to demonstrate how to draw a figure with a line of symmetry.
- Ask, *How are the two sides of the figure similar? How are they different?* (The size and shape of both sides match, but they are "opposite.")
- Ask students to draw symmetric figures or images on dot paper. Have them draw the line of symmetry in each.
- Ask, *How could you draw a symmetrical house on dot paper?*

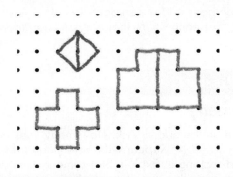

Activity 12 (Lesson 11-3)

Drawing more shapes using lines of symmetry

- Use Dot Paper (Teaching Tool 17) to draw half of a symmetrical figure and its line of symmetry. Ask a volunteer to draw the other half and describe the figure drawn.
- Have students work in pairs. One partner will draw half of a symmetrical figure and its line of symmetry. The other will complete the image and describe the figure drawn. Have partners switch roles several times.
- Ask, *What objects in nature, at home, or in school do you know that are symmetrical?* (Butterflies, eyeglasses)

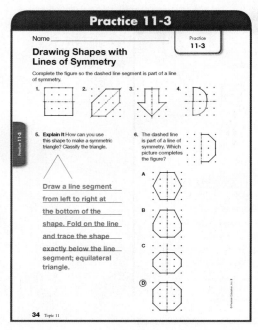

Use after the **Lesson 11-3** activities.

Activity 13 (Lesson 11-4)

Finding symmetry with tangrams

- Explain to students that a tangram is a large square made up of seven smaller shapes. Show students Tangram Pieces (Teaching Tool 37) and ask them to identify the shapes.
- Ask, *Which of these shapes have lines of symmetry?* (the triangles and the square)
- *Do any of the shapes have more than one line of symmetry?* (the square) *Do any have more than two lines of symmetry?* (the square) Have students work in pairs to trace the shapes and draw as many lines of symmetry as they can for each shape.

Activity 14 (Lesson 11-4)

Use objects

- Make a rectangle using Tangram Pieces as shown. Ask, *What shape did I make?* (A rectangle) *What shapes did I use?* (A parallelogram, square, and two small triangles.)

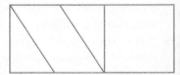

- *How can you make another shape using these four tangram pieces?* (Move the shapes to form another shape.)
- Provide students with Tangram Pieces (Teaching Tool 37). Have pairs make any three shapes using their pieces.

Activity 15 (Lesson 11-4)

Make symmetrical shapes with tangrams

- Guide students to use Tangram Pieces (Teaching Tool 37) to make several shapes with at least one line of symmetry. Ask students to draw each of the shapes they made.
- Ask, *How can you find a shape's line of symmetry?* (Find the line that makes the two halves match when the paper is folded.) Have pairs draw the lines of symmetry on each other's shapes.

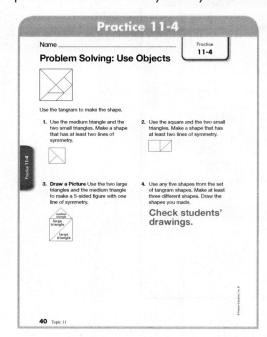

Use after the **Lesson 11-4** activities.

Understanding measurement

- Demonstrate how to use your hand to measure the length of a student's textbook. Have students measure their books with their own hands and discuss their results.
- Ask, *Is everybody's measurement the same?* (No, the number of hand-lengths is different.) *Why is there a difference in the number of hand-lengths?* (The size of people's hands varies.)
- Demonstrate how to use an object with a fixed length, such as a paperclip, to measure. Have students measure the length of their books with this object. Elicit that their measurements are all the same because the objects they are using are the same size.

Measuring length in inches

- Demonstrate how to use a ruler to measure length in inches.
- Ask students to estimate and then to measure the length of several common objects, such as pencils, in inches. Tell them to use the lengths of the items they already know to estimate lengths.
- When students have completed their measurements, lead them in a discussion of the steps they took to estimate and measure.

Drawing length in inches

- Ask, *How can you draw a line segment that is 1 inch long?* (Start at the 0-inch mark and draw along the ruler to the 1-inch mark.)
- Have each student draw three line segments of different lengths.
- Have students switch papers with a partner, measure each other's line segments, and label each segment with its length in inches.

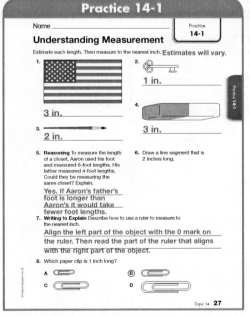

Use after the **Lesson 14-1** activities.

Measuring length to the nearest $\frac{1}{2}$ inch

- Provide inch rulers to each student. Ask, *Where are the $\frac{1}{2}$-inch marks?* (Halfway between the inch marks) *How can you measure an object to the nearest $\frac{1}{2}$ inch?* (Accept reasonable explanations.)
- Have students use a ruler to measure several classroom objects to the nearest $\frac{1}{2}$ inch. Then have them exchange objects with a partner and check each other's measurements.

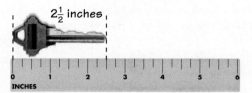

Measuring length to the nearest $\frac{1}{4}$ inch

- Provide inch rulers to each student. Ask, *Where are the $\frac{1}{4}$-inch marks?* (Halfway between each inch and $\frac{1}{2}$-inch mark, and the $\frac{1}{2}$-inch mark itself) *How can you measure an object to the nearest $\frac{1}{4}$ inch?* (Accept reasonable explanations.)
- Ask students to measure the same objects they did in Activity 19, but to the nearest $\frac{1}{4}$ inch. Ask, *Are any of the measurements the same when you measured to the nearest $\frac{1}{4}$ inch as when you measured to the nearest $\frac{1}{2}$ inch?* (Some students should have measurements that are the same.) *Why are the measurements the same?* (The $\frac{1}{2}$-inch mark is also a $\frac{1}{4}$-inch mark.)

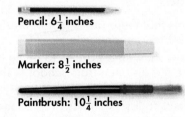

Pencil: $6\frac{1}{4}$ inches

Marker: $8\frac{1}{2}$ inches

Paintbrush: $10\frac{1}{4}$ inches

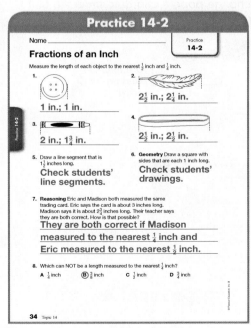

Use after the **Lesson 14-2** activities.

PACING FOR TEST SUCCESS

Activity 21 (Lesson 14-3)

Measuring in feet and inches

- Discuss feet as units of measure, explaining that there are 12 inches in 1 foot. Ask, *How can you find the number of inches in 2 feet?* (Multiply the number of feet, 2, by the number of inches in a foot, 12; 24) *How many inches are in 3 feet?* (36)
- Demonstrate how to use a ruler to measure the length of objects that are longer than 12 inches.
- Have students work in small groups to measure the length of classroom furniture in feet and inches.

Activity 22 (Lesson 14-3)

Inches, feet, yards, and miles

- On the board, write the equivalent measures shown.
- Discuss how to show equivalent lengths by multiplying and adding.
- *How can you say 2 feet, 5 inches in inches only?* (1 foot = 12 inches, 2 feet = 24 inches, 24 inches + 5 inches = 29 inches)

12 inches	= 1 foot (ft)
3 feet	= 1 yard (yd)
36 inches	= 1 yard
5,280 feet	= 1 mile (mi)
1,760 yards	= 1 mile

- Have students work in pairs to write the lengths of the furniture they measured in Activity 21 in inches.

Activity 23 (Lesson 14-3)

Yards or miles

- Remind students that there are 3 feet in one yard and 1,760 yards, or 5,280 feet, in one mile.
- Have students work with a partner to name the unit they would use to measure the distance from school to the ocean, the length of a soccer field, and the distance between two cities.
- Then ask students to list examples of three more distances or lengths. Invite them to exchange papers and determine the unit they would use to measure each distance or length.

Use after the **Lesson 14-3** activities.

Activity 24 (Lesson 14-4)

Using cups, pints, quarts, and gallons

- Display cup, pint, quart, and gallon containers. Explain that each represents a customary unit of capacity. Write the following on the board: 1 pint = 2 cups, 1 quart = 2 pints, and 1 gallon = 4 quarts.
- Ask, *How many pints are in one gallon? How do you know?* (8; Multiply the number of pints in a quart, 2, by the number of quarts in a gallon, 4.) *How many cups are in one quart?* (4)
- Have students work in small groups to come up with at least one item that typically comes in each of the units listed above. Encourage groups to share their items with the class.

Activity 25 (Lesson 14-4)

Estimating cups, pints, quarts, and gallons

- Review the relationship between cups, pints, quarts, and gallons.
- Have students work in small groups to create a list of five containers and a separate list of the corresponding estimates of their capacities. Tell students to write each of their lists in a different order.
- Ask groups to exchange papers. Each group should try to match the items on the list of containers with the correct estimates of their capacity.

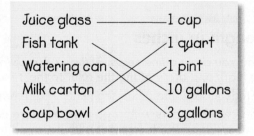

- When groups are finished working, have volunteers discuss their reasoning for matching items on the lists.

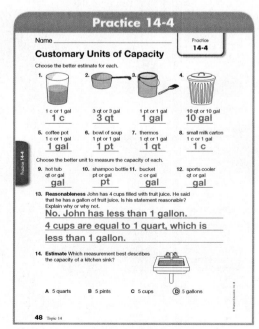

Use after the **Lesson 14-4** activities.

Activity 26 (Lesson 14-5)

Customary units of weight

- Display a cracker, a loaf of bread, and a picture of a car. Explain that the cracker weighs about 1 ounce, the bread weighs about 1 pound, and the car weighs about 1 ton.
- On the board, write, *dog, horse, stuffed animal*. Ask, *What unit would you use to weigh each of these items?* (pounds, tons, ounces)
- Have students work in pairs to find items around the classroom that weigh about 1 pound. Encourage them to check their estimates by weighing each item they choose on a pan balance.

Activity 27 (Lesson 14-5)

Using ounces, pounds, and tons

- Review the customary units of weight with students.
- Ask, *What unit would you use to weigh an apple?* (ounces) *A car?* (tons) *A bowling ball?* (pounds)
- Draw the table shown on the board. Beside the table, write the following in list form: paperback book, dog, bicycle, bear, lemon, popcorn, fish tank, van.

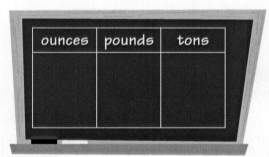

ounces	pounds	tons

- Have students work in small groups to determine the best unit to measure each item. Have groups copy and complete the table, writing each item in the correct column.

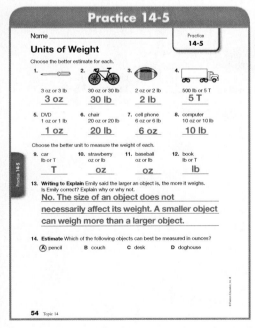

Use after the **Lesson 14-5** activities.

Activity 28 (Lesson 14-6)

Front, side, and top views

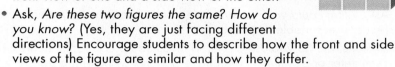

- Use Base Ten Unit Cubes to build the figure shown twice. Orient the figures so that students see a front view of one and a side view of the other.
- Ask, *Are these two figures the same? How do you know?* (Yes, they are just facing different directions) Encourage students to describe how the front and side views of the figure are similar and how they differ.
- *You can draw different views of a figure to tell what the figure looks like.* Have students work in pairs to draw front, side, and top views of the figure.

Activity 29 (Lesson 14-6)

Act it out

- Distribute several Base Ten Unit Cubes to each student. Ask students to use the cubes to build simple figures.
- Ask, *How can you draw the front, side, and top views of your figure?* (Accept reasonable responses) Ask students to draw the front, side, and top views of their figures.
- Have students look at a partner's figures. Ask them to draw the front, side, and top views of their partner's figure. Then have partners compare their drawings to check their work.

Activity 30 (Lesson 14-6)

Act it out and use reasoning

- Ask, *How can you use drawings of the front, side, and top views of a figure to build that figure?* (match the cubes to the drawings)
- Distribute Base Ten Unit Cubes to students and have them build simple figures with them. Ask students to draw the front, side, and top views of their figures.
- Have students exchange papers with a partner. Guide students to use their partners' drawings to build the figure. Repeat the activity if time permits.

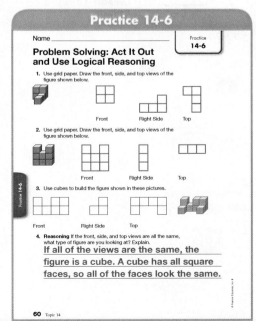

Use after the **Lesson 14-6** activities.

PACING FOR TEST SUCCESS

PACING FOR TEST SUCCESS

Centimeters and decimeters

- Distribute centimeter rulers to students and guide them as they study the marks on their rulers. *A centimeter is a metric unit of measure for length. A decimeter is 10 centimeters long.*
- Ask, *What could you measure using centimeters or decimeters?* (Accept reasonable responses.)
- Demonstrate how to use a ruler to measure objects to the nearest centimeter or decimeter. Then have students work with a partner to measure objects around the classroom and record their work.

Estimating length in centimeters

- Distribute centimeter rulers to students.
- Have students estimate the length of four objects in the room in centimeters. Ask students to sketch the objects, write estimates, and exchange papers with a partner. Partners measure the objects with a ruler to check the estimates.

Width of finger: 1cm

Length of piece of chalk: 7cm

Width of book: 15 cm

Width of backpack: 3 dm

Comparing centimeters and decimeters

- Distribute centimeter rulers to students.
- Have students measure an object that is about 20 centimeters long and one that is about 2 decimeters long. Ask, *Are these objects the same length?* (Yes, 20 centimeters is equal to 2 decimeters.)
- Divide the class into small groups. Have groups find, list, and measure objects around the classroom in decimeters. Groups then exchange papers and rewrite their measurements in centimeters.

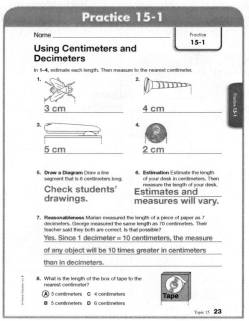

Use after the **Lesson 15-1** activities.

Estimating meters and kilometers

- Display a meter stick and explain that a meter is equal to 100 centimeters. Then explain that a kilometer is equal to 1,000 meters.
- Ask, *Is the length of a swing set greater than or less than 1 kilometer?* Explain. (Less than 1 kilometer; a kilometer is much longer than a swing set.)
- Have students find objects around the classroom that are about 1 meter long. Then ask them to name or describe distances that can be measured in kilometers.

Converting meters and kilometers

- Draw the table shown on the board.

kilometers	1	2	3	4	5
meters	1,000	2,000			

- Have students copy and complete the table. Ask, *How can this table help you rewrite kilometers as meters?* (I can quickly see how many meters there are in different numbers of kilometers)
- Ask, *How many meters are there in 3 kilometers, 52 meters?* (3,052 meters)
- Have students write several distances in kilometers. Then have them exchange papers with a partner. Partners should rewrite one another's distances in meters. Guide them to use their charts to help, if necessary.

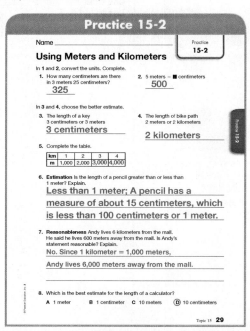

Use after the **Lesson 15-2** activities.

Metric units of capacity

- Display a liter bottle and a bottle cap. Explain that *liters* and *milliliters* are metric units of capacity.
- On the board, write the equivalence *1 liter = 1,000 milliliters*.
- Ask students to find containers, such as bottles of glue and decide whether the containers would best be measured in milliliters or liters. Have them look at the labels to check their answer.

Choosing milliliters and liters

- Review the relationship between milliliters and liters. *Which unit is larger?* (liters) *How many milliliters are in one liter?* (1,000)
- Display several containers. *How can you choose a unit to measure each container?* Ask students to choose the better unit to measure the capacity of each container.

spoon   **eyedropper**   **water bottle**   **pail**

Estimating capacities

- Display a 2-liter container. *What is a better estimate of the capacity of this container, 2 milliliters or 2 liters?* (2 liters; I can think of a 1-liter container. Since this is bigger, it holds more.)
- Have students write down two options for several containers' capacity. Ask partners to exchange papers and circle the best estimate.

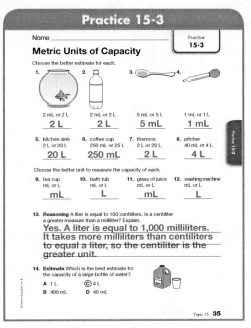

Use after the **Lesson 15-3** activities.

Metric units of mass

- Display a paper clip and a textbook. Explain that the mass of a paper clip is about 1 gram and that a textbook could have a mass of about 1 kilogram.
- On the board, write the equivalence *1 kilogram = 1,000 grams*.
- Have students work in small groups to find several items around the classroom that would best be measured in grams and several items that would best be measured in kilograms.
- Discuss students' items and ask how they decided which unit of measure they would use.

Using grams and kilograms

- Review the relationship between grams and kilograms.
- Display several grocery items with different masses, such as a box of raisins, a box of crackers, a granola bar, and a package of flour. For each item, give students an option between a mass in grams and a mass in kilograms. For example, ask, *Does this item have a mass of 2 grams or 2 kilograms?* Ask students to choose the best estimate and explain their answer.
- Have students work in pairs to write two options of mass for items around the classroom. Discuss students' options as a class and ask volunteers to choose the best estimate for each item.

Grocery List

5 kilograms of grapes

1 kilogram of cheese

500 grams of crackers

4 liters of juice

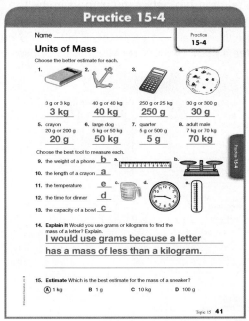

Use after the **Lesson 15-4** activities.

PACING FOR TEST SUCCESS

Make a table and look for a pattern

- Copy the table shown on the board.
- Ask, *What does the top row show?* (The number of bricks) *What does the bottom row show?* (The total length of the bricks)

Number of Bricks	1	2	3	4	5	6
Length (cm)	6	12	18			

- *How long are the bricks if there are 2 end-to-end?* (12 cm long) *Three bricks end-to-end?* (18 cm long) *How can you find whether or not there is a pattern for the total length of the bricks?* (Relate the numbers in the bottom row to those in the top row)
- Have students work in pairs to copy and complete the table.

Make a table and look for a pattern

- Remind students of how they found a pattern in Activity 41.
- Pose the following problem: *Rita is cutting a piece of yarn that is 56 centimeters long into pieces that are each 7 centimeters long. What is the length of yarn left after Rita has made 3 cuts? 4 cuts?*
- Draw the following table and have students copy it.

Number of cuts	0	1	2	3	4
Length Left (cm)	56	49	42		

- *How can you look for a pattern to complete this table and solve the problem?* (Find the relationship between numbers in the top and bottom rows.) Have students complete the table.
- Ask, *How did you know there were 35 centimeters left after 3 cuts and 28 centimeters after 4 cuts?* (Accept reasonable responses.)

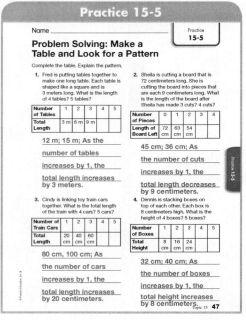

Use after the **Lesson 15-5** activities.

Perimeter on a grid

- Draw a six-sided figure along the grid lines of Centimeter Grid Paper (Teaching Tool 13) and hold it up for students to see. Review the meaning of perimeter with students. *If each unit on this grid paper represents 1 meter, how can you find the perimeter of this figure?* Demonstrate how to count the unit segments to find the perimeter.
- Provide Centimeter Grid Paper to students and ask them to draw a rectangle on it. Have students exchange papers and find the perimeter of each other's rectangles by counting the unit segments.

Perimeter as sum of sides

- Draw a trapezoid on the board and label each side as shown.
- Ask, *How can you find the perimeter of this figure?* (Add the lengths of each side.) As a class, add the lengths of the sides to find the perimeter.

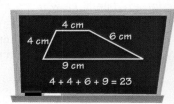

- Ask students to draw a polygon, label the lengths of the sides, and switch papers with partners to find the perimeter by adding the lengths of the sides.

Perimeter

- Pose the following problem: *The farmer wants to make a coop for her chickens and put a fence around it. The coop will have 5 sides with lengths of 6 meters, 6 meters, 8 meters, 10 meters, and 8 meters. What is the perimeter of the coop?* (38 meters) Have students explain how they found their answers.
- Ask students to write a word problem involving finding perimeter. Have partners exchange papers and solve one another's problems.

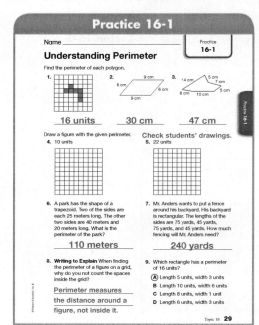

Use after the **Lesson 16-1** activities.

Perimeter of common shapes

- Review perimeter with students. Ask, *What is the perimeter of a figure?* (The distance around it.) Draw a square on the board and label each side *7 cm*. Ask, *How can you find the perimeter of this square?* (Add all 4 sides; multiply 7 by 4.) *What is the perimeter of the square?* (28 cm)
- Have students draw a rectangle and a triangle and label each side with a measurement. Then have students exchange papers and find the perimeter of one another's figures.

Perimeter of squares and rectangles

- Remind students how to find the perimeter of a figure by adding the lengths of its sides.
- Review properties of squares and rectangles. Ask, *How many sides of a square have the same measure? How many sides of a rectangle?* (all four sides; two pairs of opposite sides)
- Ask, *Suppose you need to find the perimeter of a square. Do you need to be given the measure of all four sides? Do you need to be given the measure of all four sides of a rectangle? Explain.* (No, all four sides of a square have the same measure; no, opposite sides of a rectangle have the same measure.)
- Draw the rectangle shown on the board. Ask, *How can you find the perimeter of this rectangle?* (Add each side twice.)
- Ask students to draw one square and one rectangle and then exchange papers with a partner. Have partners use centimeter rulers to measure one side of the square and two sides of the rectangle. Then ask them to use their measurements to find the perimeters of the figures.

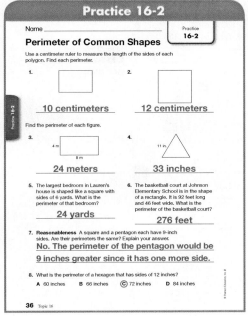

Different rectangles with the same perimeter

- Provide Centimeter Grid Paper (Teaching Tool 13). Ask, *How can you draw a rectangle with a perimeter of 14 cm?* (Decide how long each side will be, remembering opposite sides are equal.) Have students draw a rectangle with a perimeter of 14 cm on their grid paper. Discuss the different rectangles students drew.
- Have students draw a rectangle with a perimeter of 18 cm. Have them discuss their rectangles in small groups.

Different shapes with the same perimeter

- Draw the figures shown on the board. Explain that shapes other than rectangles can also have the same perimeter.
- Challenge students to draw shapes other than rectangles with perimeters of 20 cm and with perimeters of 16 cm. Discuss figures as a class, emphasizing the variety of shapes.

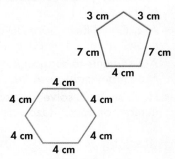

More about different shapes with the same perimeter

- Draw the figures from Activity 49 on the board again.
- *Are these figures the same?* (No, one has 5 sides and one has 6 sides.) *Do they have the same perimeter?* (Yes, both have a perimeter of 24 cm.)
- Ask, *How can you draw two different figures that have the same perimeter?* (Accept reasonable responses.)
- Challenge pairs to draw two different figures, each with a perimeter of 26 cm, then two different figures with perimeters of 30 cm.

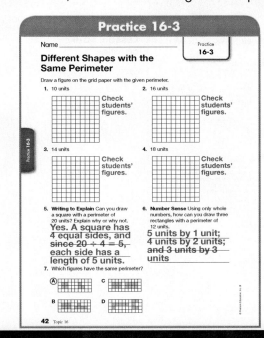

Use after the **Lesson 16-2** activities.

Use after the **Lesson 16-3** activities.

Activity 51 (Lesson 16-4)

Try, check, and revise

- Tell students that one way to solve some problems is to try a solution, check the answer, and revise if necessary. *Reza and Mia collected 60 cans in all for a recycling drive. Reza has 10 more cans than Mia. How many cans does Reza have?*
- Draw the model shown on the board. *You can use a model to help.*

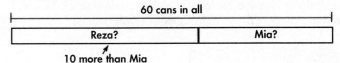

- *What do you know about the number of cans that each girl collected?* (Reza collected 10 more cans than Mia; they collected 60 cans in all.)
- Ask, *Could Reza have 30 cans and Mia 20 cans? How do you know?* (No, 30 + 20 = 50 and they collected 60 cans)
- Ask students to suggest numbers until they find the correct sum. *How many cans does Reza have?* (35)
- Have students solve the problem again, with 74 as the total number of cans. (Reza has 42 cans.)

Activity 52 (Lesson 16-4)

More about try, check, and revise

- Pose the following problem: *Ken, Marcy, and Juan bought 35 apples. Ken bought 2 more than Marcy. Juan and Marcy bought the same number. How many apples did Ken buy?*
- Draw the model shown for students to use to solve the problem.

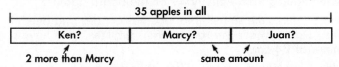

- Have students work in pairs to write their own problems that can be solved using the try, check, and revise strategy.

Activity 53 (Lesson 16-5)

Counting to find area

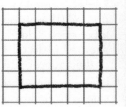

- Draw the rectangle shown and introduce *area* and *square unit*. (See page 376.) *You can find the area of a rectangle by counting the number of square units. What is the area of this rectangle?* (20 square units)
- Distribute Centimeter Grid Paper (Teaching Tool 13). Have students draw two rectangles, exchange papers with a partner, and find the area of their partner's rectangles.

Activity 54 (Lesson 16-5)

Multiplying to the area of a rectangle

- Draw and label a 6 cm by 4 cm rectangle on the board.
- *What are the length and width of this rectangle?* (6 cm and 4 cm) *How can you find the area of this rectangle?* (There will be 6 centimeters in each row. Multiply the length by the width.) *What is the area of the rectangle?* (24 sq cm)
- Have students draw and label two rectangles, exchange papers with a partner, and find the area of one another's rectangles by multiplying.

Activity 55 (Lesson 16-5)

Different shapes with the same area

- Draw and label three rectangles. The first rectangle is 2 cm by 6 cm, the second is 3 cm by 4 cm, and the third is 1 cm by 12 cm.
- Have students find the areas. *What do you notice about the areas of the rectangles?* (All have an area of 12 sq cm.)
- Provide students with Centimeter Grid Paper (Teaching Tool 13). Have them work in small groups to draw as many rectangles as they can with areas of 24 sq units and 18 sq units.

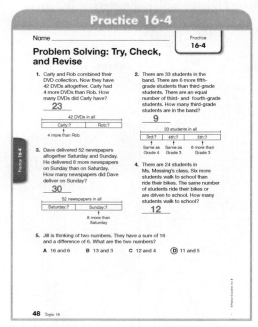

Use after the **Lesson 16-4** activities.

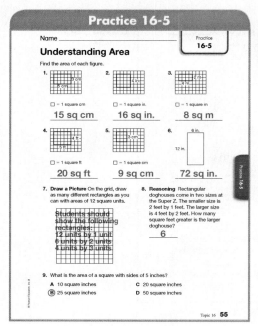

Use after the **Lesson 16-5** activities.

Finding the area of an irregular shape

- Review *area* with students. *What are two ways you can find the area of a rectangle?* (Count the square units; multiply sides)
- Draw this shape on the board. *How can you find the area of this shape?* (Count the square units.) Elicit that since the shape is not a rectangle, they cannot simply multiply the length by the width. *What is the area of this shape?* (7 sq units)
- Distribute Centimeter Grid Paper (Teaching Tool 13). Ask students to draw two irregular shapes, making sure they draw only on the lines of the grid. Have students exchange papers and find the area of the shapes.

Estimating the area of an irregular shape

- Ask, *How do you find the area of an irregular shape?* (Count the square units.) Draw this shape on the board. *How can you find the area of this shape?* (Accept reasonable responses.)
- Guide students to count the whole square units first. *How many whole square units are there?* (8) *Can you stop once you've counted the whole units?* (No, the shape covers more than just the whole units.) *How can you estimate the area of the partial squares?* (They cover about half a square each, so they cover about 2 square units in all.) *What do you do now?* (Add the whole units and partial units; 10 square units.)
- Provide Centimeter Grid Paper (Teaching Tool 13). Have students draw irregular shapes and estimate the area of each.

Volume

- Use Base Ten Unit Cubes to build a rectangular solid and introduce the concepts of *volume* and *cubic units*. (See page 380.) Explain that the volume of a figure is the number of cubic units in it. Ask, *How can you find the volume of this figure?* (Count the cubes in it.)
- Provide small groups with 20 Base Ten Unit Cubes to build rectangular solids and find the volume by counting cubes.

More about volume

- Using Base Ten Unit Cubes, build a solid that is not a rectangular solid. Ask, *How can you find the volume of this solid?* (Count the cubic units)
- Provide small groups with 20 Base Ten Unit Cubes to build figures. Then have students in each group find the volume of their figures. Have groups repeat as time allows.

Finding volume

- Provide students with Base Ten Unit Cubes. *Marc made a rectangular prism with 5 layers of cubes. He put 3 cubes in each layer. What is the volume of the rectangular prism?*
- Ask, *How can you model this problem?* (Put three cubes in a row on the table. Then put four cubes on top of each of the three cubes.) Have students model with their cubes. *How can you find the volume of this figure?* (Count the cubes; the volume is 15 cubic units.)
- Have pairs create problems involving building solid figures. Encourage them to model the figures and find the volume.

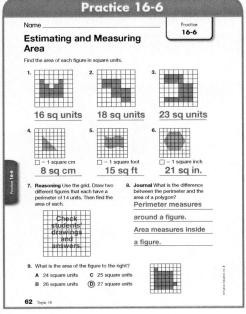

Use after the **Lesson 16-6** activities.

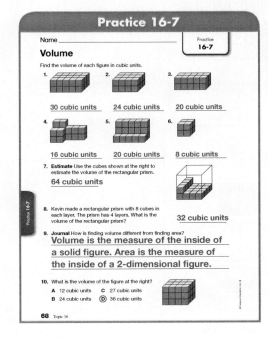

Use after the **Lesson 16-7** activities.

PACING FOR TEST SUCCESS

Activity 61 (Lesson 16-8)

Solving a simpler problem

• Draw the figure at right on the board and pose the following problem: *Mike wants to tile the floor. The shaded part of the figure shows the part of the floor that needs tiles. What is the area of the shaded part?*

• *Sometimes solving a simpler problem first can be a good way to solve a problem. Model how to solve the problem by finding the area of the whole rectangle and then the area of the square. Subtract to find the area of the shaded part.* (28 square meters)

☐ = 1 square meter

• Draw the figure below on the board. Have students copy the figure onto Centimeter Grid Paper (Teaching Tool 13) and find the area of the shaded part. (21 square meters)

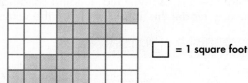

☐ = 1 square meter

Activity 62 (Lesson 16-8)

More about solving a simpler problem

• On the board, show the figure below and pose the following problem: *Ms. Winn is going to paint her kitchen wall. The shaded part of the figure is the part that needs to be painted. What is the area of the shaded part?* (20 square feet)

• Have students solve the problem. Then discuss how they solved it as a class.

☐ = 1 square foot

Activity 63 (Lesson 17-1)

Time to the half hour

• On the board, draw a clock showing 7:30. *When the minute hand is on the 6, you can say the time is "half past" the hour.* Write "7:30," "half past 7," and "30 minutes past 7" on the board.

• Then write 1:30, 5:30, and 9:30 on the board. Have students write each time in two other ways. (half past 1, 30 minutes past 1; half past 5, 30 minutes past 5; half past 9, 30 minutes past 9)

Activity 64 (Lesson 17-1)

Time to the quarter hour

• On the board, draw a clock showing the time 6:45. *When the minute hand is on the 9, you can say the time is "15 minutes to" or "quarter to" the next hour.* Write "6:45," "15 minutes to 7," and "quarter to 7" on the board.

• Draw a clock showing 8:15. *When the minute hand is on the 3, you can say the time is "15 minutes past" or "quarter past" the hour.* Write "8:15," "15 minutes past 8," and "quarter past 8" on the board.

• Write 5:45, 11:15, and 1:45 on the board. Have students write each time in two other ways. (quarter to 6, 15 minutes to 6; quarter past 11, 15 minutes past 11; quarter to 2, 15 minutes to 2)

Activity 65 (Lesson 17-1)

Time to the half hour and quarter hour

• Review how to read time to the half hour and quarter hour.

• Have students work in groups of three. One student writes a time to the half or quarter hour, such as 3:45. The other two students each suggest another way to write the time. Have students switch roles and repeat the activity.

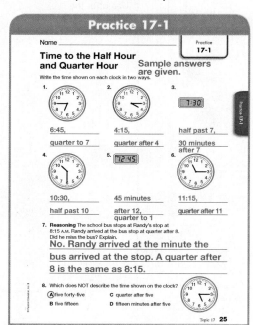

Use after the **Lesson 17-1** activities.

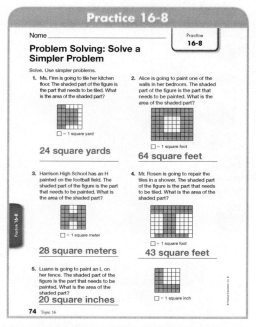

Use after the **Lesson 16-8** activities.

Activity 66 (Lesson 17-2)

Time to 5 minutes

• Draw an analog clock face showing 2:20 on the board. Model how to read the time. *What two numbers is the hour hand between?* (2 and 3) *So, the time is after 2 but before 3. How can you find how many minutes past 2 it is?* Elicit that students can skip count by 5s from one number to the next on the clock face. Model skip counting by 5s to 20. (See page 397.)

• Draw clock faces showing 7:10, 9:55, and 1:35 on the board. Have students record the times on a separate sheet of paper.

Activity 67 (Lesson 17-2)

Time to the minute

• Draw an analog clock face showing 5:38 on the board. Model how to read the time to the minute by skip counting by 5s and counting on by 1s. (See page 397.)

• Then draw clock faces showing 4:23, 12:59, and 6:11 on the board. Have students record the times on a separate sheet of paper.

Activity 68 (Lesson 17-2)

Ways to write the time

• Draw an analog clock face showing 3:47 on the board. Model how to read the time in three ways. *The time is 3:47, 47 minutes past 3, or 13 minutes to 4.*

• Then draw clock faces showing 9:06, 10:53, and 3:34 on the board. Have students write each time in two ways. (9:06, six past 9; 10:53, 53 minutes past 10, 7 minutes to 11; 3:34, 34 minutes past 3, 26 minutes to 3)

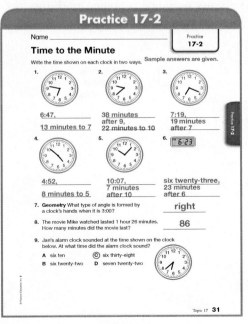

Use after the **Lesson 17-2** activities.

Activity 69 (Lesson 17-3)

Units of time

• Write the relationships shown below on the board.

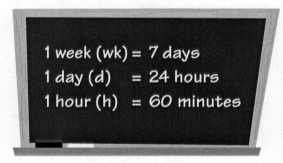

1 week (wk) = 7 days
1 day (d) = 24 hours
1 hour (h) = 60 minutes

• *You know there are 7 days in 1 week. You can find how many days are in 8 weeks by multiplying 7 times 8.* On the board, write 7 days × 8 = _____ days. *How many days are in 8 weeks?* (56 days)

• Have each student find the number of minutes in 2 hours and the number of hours in three days. (120 minutes; 72 hours)

• Then have students work with partners to find the number of minutes in 4 hours, 15 minutes. (255)

Activity 70 (Lesson 17-3)

Solving problems with time

• Review how to change units of time.

• Pose the following problems for pairs of students to solve.

• *Yolanda is building a treehouse. The project will last for 5 weeks. How many days are in 5 weeks?* (35)

• *Tom is building a model plane. The project will last 3 hours. How many minutes will it take him to build the plane?* (180 minutes)

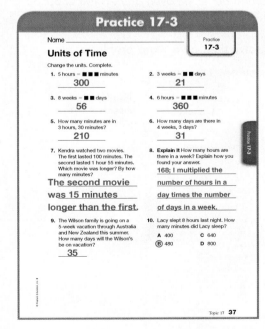

Use after the **Lesson 17-3** activities.

PACING FOR TEST SUCCESS

Elapsed time

- Discuss *elapsed time* with students. (See page 400.) Draw the clocks shown on the board. *The party started at 5:00 P.M. and ended at 8:45 P.M. How long was the party?*

- Have students guide you to use a Pupil's Clock Face from the Manipulative Kit. Count the hours, then minutes, between the starting and ending times.

- Have small groups use Pupil's Clock Faces to find the elapsed times between 3:00 P.M. and 9:15 P.M., 4:30 P.M. and 7:15 P.M., and 1:10 P.M. and 7:20 P.M. (6 h 15 m; 2 h 45 m; 6 h 10 m)

Finding start times

- Point out that if students know the elapsed time and the end time, they can find the start time.
- *The baseball game ended at 10:45 P.M. If it lasted 3 hours and 30 minutes, at what time did it start?* Have students instruct as you count back hours and minutes on a Pupil's Clock Face.
- Have students work in pairs to find the start times for events that end at 4:15 P.M., 6:20 P.M., and 9:00 A.M. and have an elapsed time of 3 hours and 30 minutes. (12:45 P.M.; 2:50 P.M.; 5:30 A.M.)

Solve problems with elapsed time

- Have pairs solve the problems: *Alana's piano lesson starts at 9:20 A.M. and ends at 10:10 A.M. How long is her lesson?* (50 minutes) *Raj took bread out of the oven at 5:25 P.M. It baked for 1 hour and 20 minutes. What time did he put it in the oven?* (4:05 P.M.)
- Have pairs write and solve their own word problems.

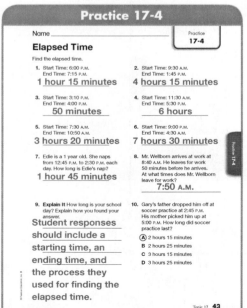

Use after the **Lesson 17-4** activities.

Temperature

- Draw the thermometer on the board as shown. Tell students that a thermometer is used to measure temperature. Refer students to the Fahrenheit and Celsius scales.
- Elicit from students that to read the thermometer, they choose the scale they need and look at the number that aligns with the shaded portion in the thermometer.
- Ask, *What temperature does this thermometer show in degrees Fahrenheit?* (40°F) *What temperature does it show in degrees Celsius?* (4°C) Shade the thermometer a little further and repeat the questions.
- Allow volunteers to come to the board and further shade the thermometer. Ask students to identify the temperature in both degrees Fahrenheit and degrees Celsius after each shading.

Fahrenheit and Celsius

- Refer students to the thermometer at the top of page 402. *At what temperature Fahrenheit does water freeze?* (32°F) *At what temperature Celsius does it freeze?* (0°C) Review all of the labeled temperatures on the thermometer.
- Ask, *If it is 10°outside and your ice melts, is it 10°F or 10°C? How do you know?* (10°C; water freezes at 32°F, so ice would not melt at 10°F.)
- Have students work in small groups to write several problems that require deciding if the temperature given is in degrees Fahrenheit or degrees Celsius. Have groups exchange papers and solve each other's problems. Then discuss students' problems and answers as a class.

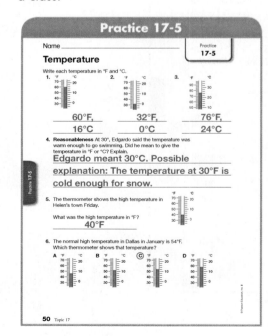

Use after the **Lesson 17-5** activities.

Work backward to solve problems involving time

- Explain that working backward is one way to solve some problems. *What time was it 15 minutes ago?* (Check answers.)
- *Rick arrives at the park at 10:00 A.M. The bus ride took 15 minutes. It took him 15 minutes to walk to the bus and 30 minutes to eat breakfast. How can you find what time Rick started eating?*
- Draw the line and the *Arrive* label on the board. Have students name the number of minutes for each activity as you complete the picture.

- Ask, *What time was it when Rick got on the bus?* (9:45 A.M.) Have students continue working backward until they reach a start time. Then change the amount of time each activity takes several times and have students find each new start time.

Work backward to solve problems involving temperature

- Ask students to work with partners to solve the following problem by drawing a picture and working backward.
- *The temperature was 62°F when Eva ate dinner at 7 P.M. The temperature was 5°F warmer at 4:00 P.M. than it was at 7 P.M. It was 3°F warmer at 1:00 P.M. than it was at 4:00 P.M. What was the temperature at 1:00 P.M?* (70°F)
- Have students work in small groups to write two problems involving working backward to find a temperature. Have a volunteer from each group pose one of their questions aloud and work backward as a class to solve it.

Complete a tally chart

- Refer students to the top of pages 458 and 459 and discuss the terms *data* and *tally*. Draw the incomplete tally chart.
- *How many people chose swimming as their favorite activity?* (12) Have students guide you to make 12 tally marks in the chart.
- Tell students that 6 people chose biking and 4 chose camping. Provide them with Tally Charts (Teaching Tool 10) and have pairs copy and complete the tally chart from the board.

Favorite Summer Activity		
Activity	Tally	Number
swimming		12
biking		
camping		

Make a tally chart to organize data

- Write the data shown on the board.
- Distribute Tally Charts (Teaching Tool 10). Have students work in small groups to organize the data in their tally charts. Discuss how they decide what to put in each column and row.

Bus	Car	Bus
Car	Car	Bike
Bike	Bus	Car
Bus	Bus	Bus
Walk	Walk	Bus
Bus	Car	Walk

Organizing and interpreting data

- Rewrite the data from Activity 79 on the board, adding another column of survey responses. Distribute Tally Charts (Teaching Tool 10) to students and have them make a tally chart to organize the data.
- Ask, *How many students ride a bus to school? How many students walk to school?* (Answers will vary.) Have volunteers ask questions that can be answered by interpreting their tally charts.

Practice 17-6

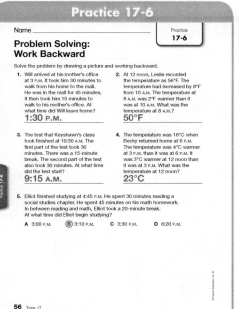

Use after the **Lesson 17-6** activities.

Practice 20-1

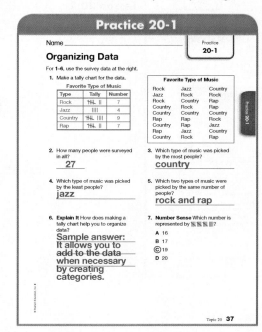

Use after the **Lesson 20-1** activities.

PACING FOR TEST SUCCESS

Reading pictographs

- Discuss the terms *pictograph* and *key* while referring to the pictograph on page 460. Ask, *How does the pictograph show the number of teams?* (Each picture of a hockey stick represents one team, and each picture of two hockey sticks represents two teams.)

- Ask, *How can you find the number of teams in the West Falls League?* (Count the number of hockey sticks. There are 11 hockey sticks, so there are 11 teams.) *How many hockey teams does each of the remaining leagues have?* (East Falls has 7; North Falls has 5; South Falls has 4) *How many teams are there altogether?* (27)

- Have students work in small groups to write and answer several questions that can be solved using the pictograph.

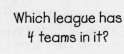

Which league has 4 teams in it?

Reading bar graphs

- Discuss the terms *bar graph* and *scale* while referring to the bar graph on page 460. Ask, *How does the bar graph show the number of goals?* (The height of each bar aligns with the number of goals that player scored.)

- *How can you find the number of goals Jack scored?* (Locate the number that aligns with the top of the bar for Jack; Jack scored 4 goals.)

- Have students write the number of goals scored by each player. (Alex scored 8; Cindi scored 7; Jack scored 4; and Reggie scored 8.) Then have them work in small groups to write and answer several more questions that can be answered using the bar graph.

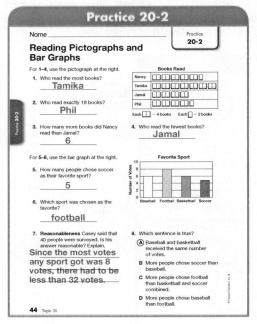

Use after the **Lesson 20-2** activities.

Completing a pictograph

- Review the parts of a pictograph with students. (See page 460.) Draw the incomplete pictograph. *The pictograph will show how many cups of lemonade different grades sold at the fair.*

- *How can you find how many cups of lemonade the third grade sold?* (Look at the lemons; there are $4\frac{1}{2}$ lemons; sold 36 cups.)

- Have students complete the pictograph with the following: fourth grade, 56 cups; fifth grade, 28 cups; sixth grade, 52 cups.

Cups of Lemonade Sold

Third Grade	🍋 🍋 🍋 🍋 ◖
Fourth Grade	
Fifth Grade	
Sixth Grade	

Each 🍋 = 8 cups
Each ◖ = 4 cups

Making a pictograph

- Copy the following tally chart on the board.

- Ask students to make a pictograph to display the data. Elicit from students how to choose a symbol to assign a number of helmets to the symbol. *How did you know how many symbols to draw to show the blue helmets sold?* (Accept reasonable explanations.)

Colors of Bicycle Helmets Sold		
Color of Helmet	**Tally**	**Number**
red	卌 卌	10
blue	卌 II	7
yellow	IIII	4
black	卌 卌 I	11

More about making a pictograph

- Redraw the tally chart from Activity 84, but change the numbers in each row. *Make a pictograph to display the data.*

- Have groups write several questions that can be answered using the pictograph. Ask volunteers to pose questions.

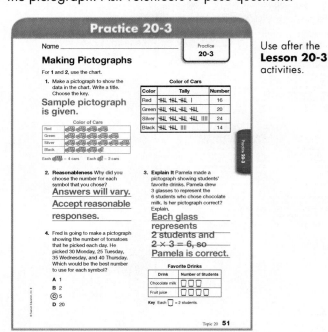

Use after the **Lesson 20-3** activities.

Completing a bar graph

- Review parts of bar graphs with students. (See page 460.) Draw the incomplete bar graph on the board as shown. Ask, *What will this bar graph show?* (The numbers of play tickets sold by students.)
- *How can you find the number of tickets Pellie sold?* (Find the number that aligns with the top of the bar for Pellie; 20 tickets)
- Distribute Centimeter Grid Paper (Teaching Tool 13) to students. Tell them that Roy sold 25 tickets, Janice sold 10 tickets, and Sandip sold 40 tickets. Ask students to complete the bar graph, guiding them as needed.

Play Tickets Sold

(Bar graph with y-axis labeled Tickets from 0 to 50, x-axis labeled Students: Pellie, Roy, Janice, Sandip. Pellie bar at 20.)

Making a bar graph

- Review how to draw bars to complete a bar graph. *How do you know how high to draw a bar?* (Draw it so that the top aligns with the number you are trying to show.) Copy the table on the board as shown.

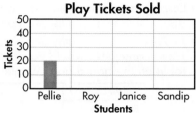

Favorite After-School Activities	
Activity	Number of Votes
Sports	10
Crafts	4
Games	6

- Distribute Centimeter Grid Paper (Teaching Tool 13) to students. Have them work in small groups to make a bar graph for the data in the table. Ask volunteers to explain how to draw the axes of a bar graph as they work. Encourage students to explain how to choose a title and scale for their graph and how to label the horizontal axis.
- Once students have completed their bar graphs, ask questions such as, *How many students voted for Sports as their favorite after-school activity?* (10) *How many fewer voted for Crafts than for Games?* (2)

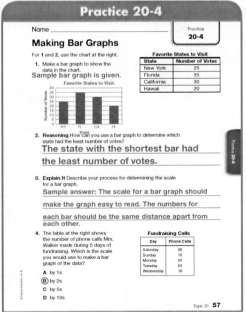

Use after the **Lesson 20-4** activities.

Ordered pairs

- Refer to the coordinate grid on top of page 468 and discuss the terms *coordinate grid* and *ordered pair* with students.
- Ask, *How can you find the location of the Birds exhibit?* (Start at 0. Move right until under *Birds*. Count the spaces moved: 2. Move up to the point. Count the spaces moved: 7; (2, 7).)
- Have students name the ordered pairs of each point of the Museum Exhibit. ((1, 9); (2, 7); (5, 4); (6, 2); (7, 8); (9, 1))

More about ordered pairs

- Distribute First-Quadrant Grids (Teaching Tool 16) to students. Have students label the grid *Downtown Locations* and plot 4 points at random labeling them *City Hall, Federal Bank, Post Office,* and *Coffee Shop.* Have students find the ordered pairs for the points.
- *How did you find the ordered pairs?* (Answers will vary.) Have students check one another's work.

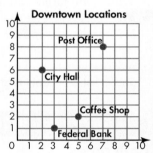

Downtown Locations

(Coordinate grid 0–10 on both axes with points: Post Office, City Hall, Coffee Shop, Federal Bank.)

Line graph

- Refer to the bottom line graph on page 468. Discuss the term *line graph.*
- Ask, *How can you find the number of sandwiches sold in the lunchroom in Week 2?* (Start at 0 and move right until reaching Week 2. Move up to the point. Move left to 60.)
- Have students find the number of sandwiches sold each week. *How did the number sold change from week 2 to week 3?* (About 10 more sandwiches were sold in week 3.)

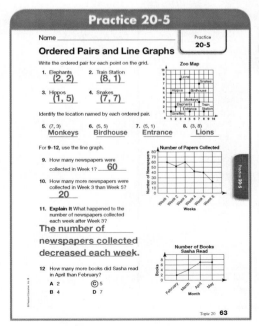

Use after the **Lesson 20-5** activities.

PACING FOR TEST SUCCESS

Activity 91 (Lesson 20-6)

Likely and unlikely

- Discuss the terms *likely* and *unlikely* with students. (See page 472.)
- Ask, *Is it likely or unlikely that you will play outside today?* (Answers will vary.) *Is it likely or unlikely that it will rain today?* (Answers will vary.)
- Have students work in small groups to write a list of events that are likely to happen and a list of events that are unlikely to happen during a field trip to a museum.

Activity 92 (Lesson 20-6)

Certain and impossible

- Discuss the terms *certain* and *impossible*. (See page 472.)
- Ask, *Is it certain or impossible that the sun will set today?* (Certain) *Is it certain or impossible you will see a living dinosaur on the way home from school?* (Impossible)
- Ask students to make a list of events that are certain to happen and a list of events that are impossible during a visit to a park.

Activity 93 (Lesson 20-6)

Outcomes

- Show a Spinner from the Manipulative Kit with four sections colored red, green, blue, and yellow. Ask, *What colors are you certain to land on?* (Red, green, blue or yellow) *What colors is it impossible for you to land on?* (Any other color.) Explain that the possibilities are *equally likely*. (See page 472.)
- Provide Spinners (Teaching Tool 23) divided into four equal sections, three blue and one yellow. Define *more likely* and *less likely*.
- Ask, *Which outcome is more likely than yellow?* (Blue) *Which outcome is less likely than blue?* (Yellow) Have students further divide their spinner, adding new colors. Have them describe more likely and less likely outcomes.

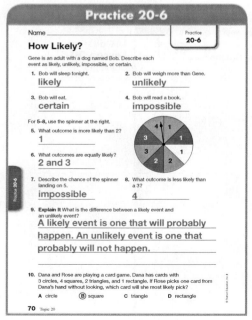

Use after the **Lesson 20-6** activities.

Activity 94 (Lesson 20-7)

Predictions

- Display a Spinner from the Manipulative Kit with 3 yellow sections and 1 blue section. Discuss the term *predict*. (See page 477.)
- *In 20 spins, how many times would you expect to land on yellow? How many times would you expect to land on blue? Copy the table on the board and complete it with students' predictions.*

Yellow					
Blue					
Total Spins	4	8	12	16	20

- Display a Spinner with 3 red sections and 2 green sections. Have students create a table to show their predictions for the results of 10 spins, 20 spins, 30 spins, 40 spins, 40 spins, and 60 spins.

Activity 95 (Lesson 20-7)

Predictions and outcomes

- Display a Spinner from the Manipulative Kit with 1 purple section and 3 green sections. *How many times do you think the spinner will land on purple if spun 20 times?* (5)
- Have students predict the results of 40, 60, 80, and 100 spins. Draw a table on their board and record their predictions. Draw the same table on the board, without the numbers and with another row at the top labeled *Test*.
- Have volunteers spin the spinner each of the number of times in the table and record the results. Discuss how students' predictions compare to the outcomes.

Test	1	2	3	4	5
Yellow	5	10	15	20	25
Blue	15	30	45	60	75
Total Spins	20	40	60	80	100

- If time allows, test the predictions made by students in Activity 94 and compare them to the outcomes.

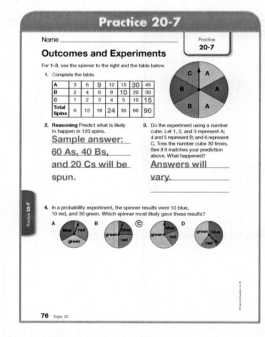

Use after the **Lesson 20-7** activities.

Read a line plot

- Guide students to read a line plot by referring them to the line plot at the top of page 478. Ask, *What do the numbers below the line represent?* (High temperatures in April in degrees Fahrenheit) *What do the Xs above the line represent?* (Each X represents one day.)
- Ask, *How can you find which high temperatures occurred twice?* (Find temperatures with two Xs; 68°F, 70°F, 72°F, 73°F) *How many days did the temperature reach 66°F or higher?* (21 days)
- Have students list three facts about the high temperatures in April.

Make a line plot

- Review how to read a line plot with students. *Mr. Wood's third grade students are eight, nine, or ten years old. There are 6 eight-year olds, 11 nine-year olds, and 2 ten-year olds. How can you make a line plot to display this?*
- Elicit how students can choose a title for their line plot, choose the numbers to write below the line, and decide where to place Xs. Have them make the line plots.

Ages of Mr. Wood's Students

```
                    x
                    x
                    x
                    x
                    x
        x           x
        x           x
        x           x
        x           x
        x           x
        x           x          x
    ----+----+----+----
        8    9    10
```

Ages in Years

Line plots and probability

- Provide pairs with a number cube labeled 2, 3, 3, 5, 5, 6. Have pairs toss the number cube 20 times and record their results.
- Ask students to make a line plot to display the results of the experiment. Discuss the likelihood of rolling each number.

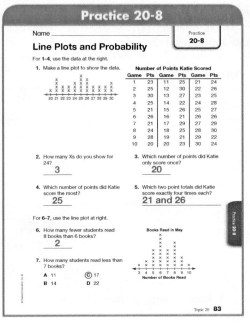

Use after the **Lesson 20-8** activities.

Use graphs to draw conclusions

- Ask students why tables and graphs can be helpful in solving problems. (The data are side-by-side, making it easier to compare.) Refer students to the bar graphs at the top of page 483.
- Ask, *What hobby do more students in Class A like than in Class B?* (Drawing) *What other comparisons can you make between the favorite hobbies of the students in Class A and Class B?* Have students work in pairs to write several comparison questions using the data in the bar graphs. Then have volunteers pose questions to the class.

Use a tally chart to write and solve problems

- Copy the tally chart shown on the board.

Students Participating in Field Day Events

Event	Tally
relay race	ⅢⅠ ⅢⅠ ⅠⅠ
ring toss	ⅢⅠ Ⅲ
ball catch	ⅢⅠ ⅢⅠ Ⅲ
long jump	ⅢⅠ ⅢⅠ ⅢⅠⅠ

- Ask, *How can you use the tally chart to find how many more students participated in the relay race than in the ring toss?* (Sample answers: Count how many more tallies there are in the row for *relay race* than in the row for *ring toss;* Find how many students participated in each event and subtract to find the difference.)
- Ask students to write two word problems that can be solved by reading the tally chart. Have students exchange papers with a partner and solve one another's problems.

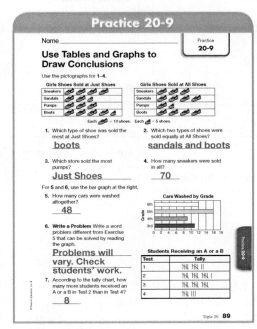

Use after the **Lesson 20-9** activities.

Lesson 1-1 **Hundreds** pp. 4–5

Lesson 1-2 **Thousands** pp. 6–7

	Hundreds (1-1)	Thousands (1-2)
Illinois Mathematics Performance Descriptors	6A.Stage C.2. Recognize equivalent representations of whole numbers and generate them by composing and decomposing numbers.	6A.Stage C.2. Recognize equivalent representations of whole numbers and generate them by composing and decomposing numbers.
Illinois Mathematics Assessment Framework Objectives	6.3.01 Read, write, recognize, and model equivalent representations of whole numbers and their place values.	6.3.01 Read, write, recognize, and model equivalent representations of whole numbers and their place values.
	Place-value blocks	Tape, place-value blocks

Teacher Resource Masters

Daily Spiral Review	Daily Spiral Review 1-1	Daily Spiral Review 1-2
Problem of the Day	Problem of the Day 1-1	Problem of the Day 1-2
Interactive Learning	Interactive Learning Recording Sheet 1	
Quick Check	Quick Check 1-1	Quick Check 1-2
Center Activities	Center Activities 1-1	Center Activities 1-2
Reteaching	Reteaching 1-1	Reteaching 1-2
Practice	Practice 1-1	Practice 1-2
Enrichment	Enrichment 1-1	Enrichment 1-2
DIGITAL www.pearsonsuccessnet.com	Animated Glossary, eTools	eTools

Topic Start-Up
- Vocabulary Card Sets A–C
- Topic 1 Home-School Connection (English and Spanish)

Topic Wrap-Up
- Topic 1 Test, pages 26–27
- Topic 1 Alternate Assessments, pages 27A–27B

- Reteaching, pages 28–29

Lesson 1-3
Greater Numbers
pp. 8–9

Lesson 1-4
Ways to Name Numbers
pp. 10–11

Lesson 1-5
Comparing Numbers
pp. 12–15

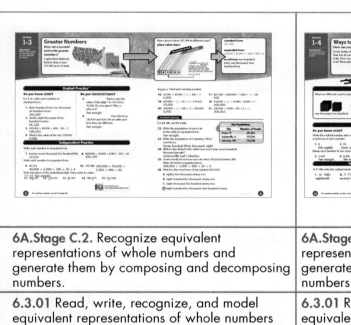

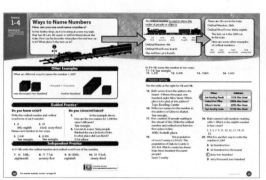

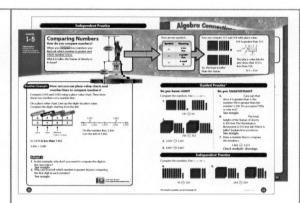

6A.Stage C.2. Recognize equivalent representations of whole numbers and generate them by composing and decomposing numbers.	**6A.Stage C.2.** Recognize equivalent representations of whole numbers and generate them by composing and decomposing numbers.	**6A.Stage C.1.** Represent, order, and compare whole numbers to demonstrate an understanding of the base-ten number system.
6.3.01 Read, write, recognize, and model equivalent representations of whole numbers and their place values.	**6.3.01** Read, write, recognize, and model equivalent representations of whole numbers and their place values.	**6.3.05** Order and compare whole numbers using symbols and words.
		Place-value blocks
Daily Spiral Review 1-3	**Daily Spiral Review 1-4**	**Daily Spiral Review 1-5**
Problem of the Day 1-3	**Problem of the Day 1-4**	**Problem of the Day 1-5**
Quick Check 1-3	**Quick Check 1-4**	**Quick Check 1-5**
Center Activities 1-3	**Center Activities 1-4**	**Center Activities 1-5**
Reteaching 1-3	**Reteaching 1-4**	**Reteaching 1-5**
Practice 1-3	**Practice 1-4**	**Practice 1-5**
Enrichment 1-3	**Enrichment 1-4**	**Enrichment 1-5**
Animated Glossary	**Animated Glossary**	**Animated Glossary**

Lesson 1-6

Ordering Numbers
pp. 16–17

Lesson 1-7

Counting Money
pp. 18–21

	Ordering Numbers (1-6)	**Counting Money** (1-7)
Illinois Mathematics Performance Descriptors	6A.Stage C.1. Represent, order, and compare whole numbers to demonstrate an understanding of the base-ten number system.	Reviews Grade 2: 7A.Stage B.6. Count, compare, and order sets of unlike coins.
Illinois Mathematics Assessment Framework Objectives	6.3.05 Order and compare whole numbers using symbols and words.	6.3.10 Solve problems involving the value of a collection of bills and coins whose total value is $10.00 or less, and make change.
	Place-value blocks	Bills and Coins (Teaching Tool 36)

Teacher Resource Masters

Daily Spiral Review	Daily Spiral Review 1-6	Daily Spiral Review 1-7
Problem of the Day	Problem of the Day 1-6	Problem of the Day 1-7
Interactive Learning	Interactive Learning Recording Sheet 2	
Quick Check	Quick Check 1-6	Quick Check 1-7
Center Activities	Center Activities 1-6	Center Activities 1-7
Reteaching	Reteaching 1-6	Reteaching 1-7
Practice	Practice 1-6	Practice 1-7
Enrichment	Enrichment 1-6	Enrichment 1-7
DIGITAL	Animated Glossary	Animated Glossary, eTools

www.pearsonsuccessnet.com

MATH STRAND COLORS

- ● Number and Operations
- ● Algebra
- ● Geometry
- ● Measurement
- ● Data Analysis and Probability
- ● Problem Solving

 Lesson 1-8

Making Change
pp. 22–23

 Lesson 1-9

Problem Solving:
Make an Organized List
pp. 24–25

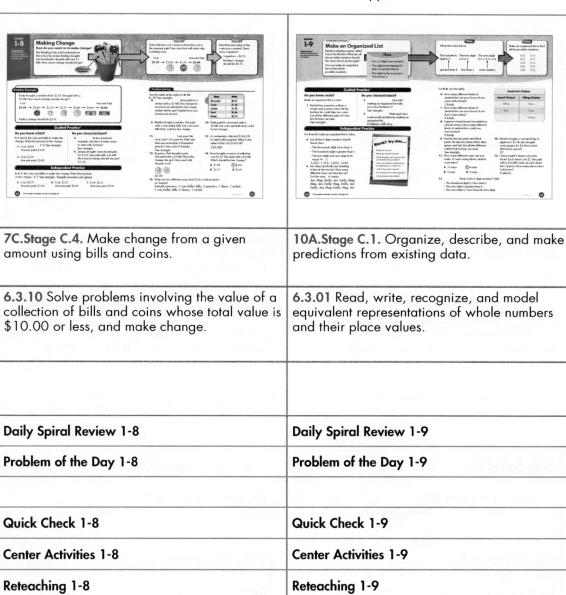

7C.Stage C.4. Make change from a given amount using bills and coins.	**10A.Stage C.1.** Organize, describe, and make predictions from existing data.
6.3.10 Solve problems involving the value of a collection of bills and coins whose total value is $10.00 or less, and make change.	**6.3.01** Read, write, recognize, and model equivalent representations of whole numbers and their place values.
Daily Spiral Review 1-8	Daily Spiral Review 1-9
Problem of the Day 1-8	Problem of the Day 1-9
Quick Check 1-8	Quick Check 1-9
Center Activities 1-8	Center Activities 1-9
Reteaching 1-8	Reteaching 1-9
Practice 1-8	Practice 1-9
Enrichment 1-8	Enrichment 1-9

Adding Whole Numbers
ILLINOIS TOPIC PLANNER   Pacing: 1 lesson per day

	Lesson 2-1 Addition Meaning and Properties pp. 32–33	**Lesson 2-2** Adding on a Hundred Chart pp. 34–35
Illinois Mathematics Performance Descriptors	**6B.Stage C.3.** Explore, identify, and use relationships between and among properties of operations.	**6C.Stage C.2.** Select appropriate methods and tools for computing with whole numbers from mental computation, estimation, calculators, and paper/pencil according to the context and nature of the computation and use of the selected method or tool.
Illinois Mathematics Assessment Framework Objectives	**8.3.04** Solve one–step addition and subtraction equations that have a missing number or missing operation sign.	**6.3.09** Solve problems and number sentences involving addition and subtraction with regrouping.
	Counters	Hundred Chart (Teaching Tool 7)
Daily Spiral Review	**Daily Spiral Review 2-1**	**Daily Spiral Review 2-2**
Problem of the Day	**Problem of the Day 2-1**	**Problem of the Day 2-2**
Interactive Learning		
Quick Check	**Quick Check 2-1**	**Quick Check 2-2**
Center Activities	**Center Activities 2-1**	**Center Activities 2-2**
Reteaching	**Reteaching 2-1**	**Reteaching 2-2**
Practice	**Practice 2-1**	**Practice 2-2**
Enrichment	**Enrichment 2-1**	**Enrichment 2-2**
www.pearsonsuccessnet.com	**Animated Glossary, eTools**	

Teacher Resource Masters

Topic Start-Up
- Vocabulary Card Sets A–B
- Topic 2 Home-School Connection (English and Spanish)

Topic Wrap-Up
- Topic 2 Test, pages 60–61
- Topic 2 Alternate Assessments, pages 61A–61B
- Reteaching, pages 62–63

MATH STRAND COLORS

- Number and Operations
- Algebra
- Geometry
- Measurement
- Data Analysis and Probability
- Problem Solving

Lesson 2-3 Using Mental Math to Add
pp. 36–39

Lesson 2-4 Rounding
pp. 40–43

Lesson 2-5 Estimating Sums
pp. 44–47

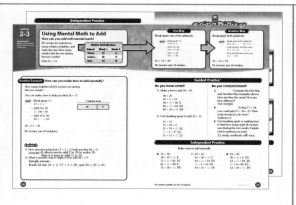

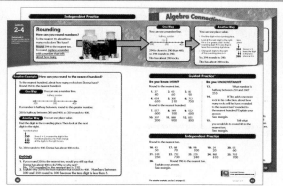

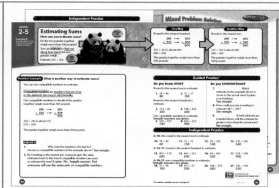

6C.Stage C.2. Select appropriate methods and tools for computing with whole numbers from mental computation, estimation, calculators, and paper/pencil according to the context and nature of the computation and use of the selected method or tool.	**6A.Stage C.1.** Represent, order, and compare whole numbers to demonstrate an understanding of the base-ten number system.	**6C.Stage C.1.** Develop and use strategies to estimate the results of whole-number computations and to judge the reasonableness of such results.
6.3.09 Solve problems and number sentences involving addition and subtraction with regrouping.	**6.3.08** Solve problems involving descriptions of numbers, including characteristics and relationships.	**6.3.14** Make estimates appropriate to a given situation with whole numbers.
Daily Spiral Review 2-3	Daily Spiral Review 2-4	Daily Spiral Review 2-5
Problem of the Day 2-3	Problem of the Day 2-4	Problem of the Day 2-5
	Interactive Learning Recording Sheet 3	Interactive Learning Recording Sheet 4
Quick Check 2-3	Quick Check 2-4	Quick Check 2-5
Center Activities 2-3	Center Activities 2-4	Center Activities 2-5
Reteaching 2-3	Reteaching 2-4	Reteaching 2-5
Practice 2-3	Practice 2-4	Practice 2-5
Enrichment 2-3	Enrichment 2-4	Enrichment 2-5
	Animated Glossary	Animated Glossary

Lesson 2-6 Adding 2-Digit Numbers pp. 48–49

Lesson 2-7 Models for Adding 3-Digit Numbers pp. 50–53

	Lesson 2-6	Lesson 2-7
Illinois Mathematics Performance Descriptors	6C.Stage C.2. Select appropriate methods and tools for computing with whole numbers from mental computation, estimation, calculators, and paper/pencil according to the context and nature of the computation and use of the selected method or tool.	6C.Stage C.2. Select appropriate methods and tools for computing with whole numbers from mental computation, estimation, calculators, and paper/pencil according to the context and nature of the computation and use of the selected method or tool.
Illinois Mathematics Assessment Framework Objectives	6.3.09 Solve problems and number sentences involving addition and subtraction with regrouping.	6.3.09 Solve problems and number sentences involving addition and subtraction with regrouping.
	Place-value blocks	Place-value blocks

Teacher Resource Masters		
Daily Spiral Review	Daily Spiral Review 2-6	Daily Spiral Review 2-7
Problem of the Day	Problem of the Day 2-6	Problem of the Day 2-7
Interactive Learning		
Quick Check	Quick Check 2-6	Quick Check 2-7
Center Activities	Center Activities 2-6	Center Activities 2-7
Reteaching	Reteaching 2-6	Reteaching 2-7
Practice	Practice 2-6	Practice 2-7
Enrichment	Enrichment 2-6	Enrichment 2-7
DIGITAL www.pearsonsuccessnet.com	eTools	eTools

MATH STRAND COLORS

- Number and Operations
- Algebra
- Geometry
- Measurement
- Data Analysis and Probability
- Problem Solving

Lesson 2-8
Adding 3-Digit Numbers
pp. 54–55

Lesson 2-9
Adding 3 or More Numbers
pp. 56–57

Lesson 2-10
Problem Solving: Draw a Picture pp. 58–59

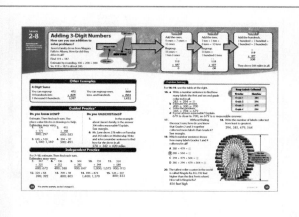

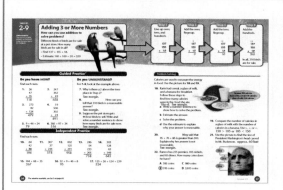

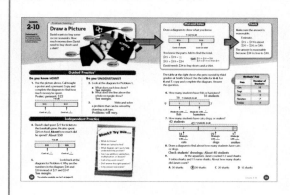

6C.Stage C.2. Select appropriate methods and tools for computing with whole numbers from mental computation, estimation, calculators, and paper/pencil according to the context and nature of the computation and use of the selected method or tool.	**6C.Stage C.2.** Select appropriate methods and tools for computing with whole numbers from mental computation, estimation, calculators, and paper/pencil according to the context and nature of the computation and use of the selected method or tool.	**6B.Stage C.7.** Select and use one of various algorithms to add and subtract.
6.3.09 Solve problems and number sentences involving addition and subtraction with regrouping.	**6.3.09** Solve problems and number sentences involving addition and subtraction with regrouping.	**8.3.05** Solve word problems involving unknown quantities.
Daily Spiral Review 2-8	**Daily Spiral Review 2-9**	**Daily Spiral Review 2-10**
Problem of the Day 2-8	**Problem of the Day 2-9**	**Problem of the Day 2-10**
	Interactive Learning Recording Sheet 5	
Quick Check 2-8	**Quick Check 2-9**	**Quick Check 2-10**
Center Activities 2-8	**Center Activities 2-9**	**Center Activities 2-10**
Reteaching 2-8	**Reteaching 2-9**	**Reteaching 2-10**
Practice 2-8	**Practice 2-9**	**Practice 2-10**
Enrichment 2-8	**Enrichment 2-9**	**Enrichment 2-10**

Subtraction Number Sense
ILLINOIS TOPIC PLANNER   Pacing: 1 lesson per day

	Lesson 3-1 Subtraction Meanings pp. 66–67	**Lesson 3-2** Subtracting on a Hundred Chart pp. 68–71
Illinois Mathematics Performance Descriptors	**6C.Stage C.2.** Select appropriate methods and tools for computing with whole numbers from mental computation, estimation, calculators, and paper/pencil according to the context and nature of the computation and use of the selected method or tool.	**6C.Stage C.2.** Select appropriate methods and tools for computing with whole numbers from mental computation, estimation, calculators, and paper/pencil according to the context and nature of the computation and use of the selected method or tool.
Illinois Mathematics Assessment Framework Objectives	**8.3.03** Represent simple mathematical relationships with number sentences (equations and inequalities).	**6.3.09** Solve problems and number sentences involving addition and subtraction with regrouping.
	Counters	Hundred Chart (Teaching Tool 7)

Teacher Resource Masters

Daily Spiral Review	Daily Spiral Review 3-1	Daily Spiral Review 3-2
Problem of the Day	Problem of the Day 3-1	Problem of the Day 3-2
Interactive Learning		
Quick Check	Quick Check 3-1	Quick Check 3-2
Center Activities	Center Activities 3-1	Center Activities 3-2
Reteaching	Reteaching 3-1	Reteaching 3-2
Practice	Practice 3-1	Practice 3-2
Enrichment	Enrichment 3-1	Enrichment 3-2
DIGITAL www.pearsonsuccessnet.com	Animated Glossary, eTools	

Topic Start-Up
- Vocabulary Cards
- Topic 3 Home-School Connection (English and Spanish)

Topic Wrap-Up
- Topic 3 Test, pages 80–81
- Topic 3 Alternate Assessments, pages 81A–81B
- Reteaching, pages 82–83

MATH STRAND COLORS

- Number and Operations
- Algebra
- Geometry
- Measurement
- Data Analysis and Probability
- Problem Solving

 Lesson 3-3 **Using Mental Math to Subtract** pp. 72–73

 Lesson 3-4 **Estimating Differences** pp. 74–77

 Lesson 3-5 **Problem Solving: Reasonableness** pp. 78–79

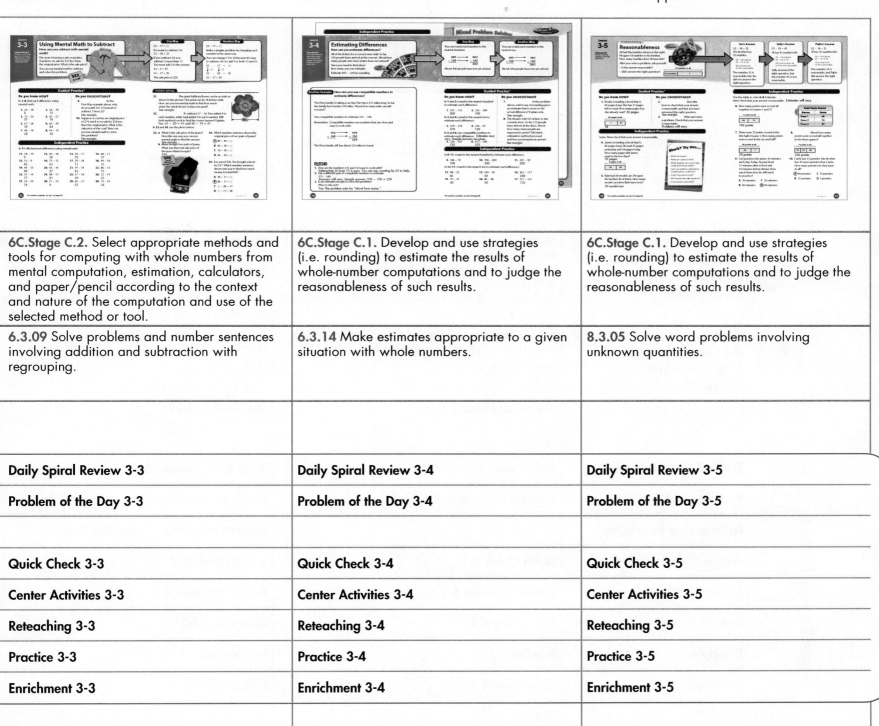

6C.Stage C.2. Select appropriate methods and tools for computing with whole numbers from mental computation, estimation, calculators, and paper/pencil according to the context and nature of the computation and use of the selected method or tool.	**6C.Stage C.1.** Develop and use strategies (i.e. rounding) to estimate the results of whole-number computations and to judge the reasonableness of such results.	**6C.Stage C.1.** Develop and use strategies (i.e. rounding) to estimate the results of whole-number computations and to judge the reasonableness of such results.
6.3.09 Solve problems and number sentences involving addition and subtraction with regrouping.	**6.3.14** Make estimates appropriate to a given situation with whole numbers.	**8.3.05** Solve word problems involving unknown quantities.
Daily Spiral Review 3-3	**Daily Spiral Review 3-4**	**Daily Spiral Review 3-5**
Problem of the Day 3-3	**Problem of the Day 3-4**	**Problem of the Day 3-5**
Quick Check 3-3	**Quick Check 3-4**	**Quick Check 3-5**
Center Activities 3-3	**Center Activities 3-4**	**Center Activities 3-5**
Reteaching 3-3	**Reteaching 3-4**	**Reteaching 3-5**
Practice 3-3	**Practice 3-4**	**Practice 3-5**
Enrichment 3-3	**Enrichment 3-4**	**Enrichment 3-5**

		Lesson 4-1 Models for Subtracting 2-Digit Numbers pp. 86–87	**Lesson 4-2** Subtracting 2-Digit Numbers pp. 88–89
	Illinois Mathematics Performance Descriptors	6C.Stage C.2. Select appropriate methods and tools for computing with whole numbers from mental computation, estimation, calculators, and paper/pencil according to the context and nature of the computation and use of the selected method or tool.	6C.Stage C.2. Select appropriate methods and tools for computing with whole numbers from mental computation, estimation, calculators, and paper/pencil according to the context and nature of the computation and use of the selected method or tool.
	Illinois Mathematics Assessment Framework Objectives	6.3.09 Solve problems and number sentences involving addition and subtraction with regrouping.	6.3.09 Solve problems and number sentences involving addition and subtraction with regrouping.
		Place-value blocks	Place-value blocks
Teacher Resource Masters	**Daily Spiral Review**	**Daily Spiral Review 4-1**	**Daily Spiral Review 4-2**
	Problem of the Day	**Problem of the Day 4-1**	**Problem of the Day 4-2**
	Interactive Learning		**Interactive Learning Recording Sheet 6**
	Quick Check	**Quick Check 4-1**	**Quick Check 4-2**
	Center Activities	**Center Activities 4-1**	**Center Activities 4-2**
	Reteaching	**Reteaching 4-1**	**Reteaching 4-2**
	Practice	**Practice 4-1**	**Practice 4-2**
	Enrichment	**Enrichment 4-1**	**Enrichment 4-2**
DIGITAL www.pearsonsuccessnet.com		eTools	

Topic Start-Up
- Topic 4 Home-School Connection (English and Spanish)

Topic Wrap-Up
- Topic 4 Test, pages 102–103
- Topic 4 Alternate Assessments, pages 103A–103B

- Reteaching, pages 104–105
- Cumulative Test Topics 1–4, pages 105A–105B
- Benchmark Test Topics 1–4, pages 105C–105D

Lesson 4-3

Models for Subtracting 3-Digit Numbers
pp. 90–91

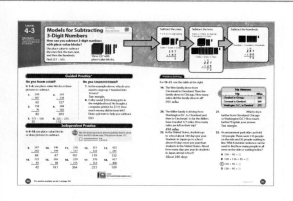

6C.Stage C.2. Select appropriate methods and tools for computing with whole numbers from mental computation, estimation, calculators, and paper/pencil according to the context and nature of the computation and use of the selected method or tool.

6.3.09 Solve problems and number sentences involving addition and subtraction with regrouping.

Place-value blocks

Daily Spiral Review 4-3

Problem of the Day 4-3

Quick Check 4-3

Center Activities 4-3

Reteaching 4-3

Practice 4-3

Enrichment 4-3

eTools

Topic 4

ILLINOIS TOPIC PLANNER   Pacing: 1 lesson per day

	Lesson 4-4 Subtracting 3-Digit Numbers pp. 92–95	**Lesson 4-5** Subtracting Across Zero pp. 96–97

Illinois Mathematics Performance Descriptors	**6C.Stage C.2.** Select appropriate methods and tools for computing with whole numbers from mental computation, estimation, calculators, and paper/pencil according to the context and nature of the computation and use of the selected method or tool.	**6C.Stage C.2.** Select appropriate methods and tools for computing with whole numbers from mental computation, estimation, calculators, and paper/pencil according to the context and nature of the computation and use of the selected method or tool.
Illinois Mathematics Assessment Framework Objectives	**6.3.09** Solve problems and number sentences involving addition and subtraction with regrouping.	**6.3.09** Solve problems and number sentences involving addition and subtraction with regrouping.
	Place-value blocks	Place-value blocks

Teacher Resource Masters

Daily Spiral Review	**Daily Spiral Review 4-4**	**Daily Spiral Review 4-5**
Problem of the Day	**Problem of the Day 4-4**	**Problem of the Day 4-5**
Interactive Learning	**Interactive Learning Recording Sheet 7**	
Quick Check	**Quick Check 4-4**	**Quick Check 4-5**
Center Activities	**Center Activities 4-4**	**Center Activities 4-5**
Reteaching	**Reteaching 4-4**	**Reteaching 4-5**
Practice	**Practice 4-4**	**Practice 4-5**
Enrichment	**Enrichment 4-4**	**Enrichment 4-5**
DIGITAL www.pearsonsuccessnet.com	eTools	

MATH STRAND COLORS

● Number and Operations   ● Measurement
● Algebra   ● Data Analysis and Probability
● Geometry   ● Problem Solving

Lesson 4-6

Problem Solving: Draw a Picture and Write a Number Sentence pp. 98–101

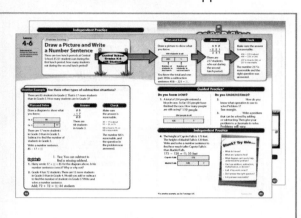

8A.Stage C.5. Express mathematical relationships using equations.

8.3.03 Represent simple mathematical relationships with number sentences (equations and inequalities).

Daily Spiral Review 4-6

Problem of the Day 4-6

Problem-Solving Recording Sheet

Quick Check 4-6

Center Activities 4-6

Reteaching 4-6

Practice 4-6

Enrichment 4-6

	Lesson 5-1 Multiplication as Repeated Addition pp. 108–109	**Lesson 5-2** Arrays and Multiplication pp. 110–113
Illinois Mathematics Performance Descriptors	6B.Stage C.5. Solve multiplication and division number sentences and word problems.	6B.Stage C.3. Explore, identify, and use relationships between and among properties of operations.
Illinois Mathematics Assessment Framework Objectives	6.3.04 Represent multiplication as repeated addition.	6.3.04 Represent multiplication as repeated addition.
	Counters	Counters
Daily Spiral Review	Daily Spiral Review 5-1	Daily Spiral Review 5-2
Problem of the Day	Problem of the Day 5-1	Problem of the Day 5-2
Interactive Learning		
Quick Check	Quick Check 5-1	Quick Check 5-2
Center Activities	Center Activities 5-1	Center Activities 5-2
Reteaching	Reteaching 5-1	Reteaching 5-2
Practice	Practice 5-1	Practice 5-2
Enrichment	Enrichment 5-1	Enrichment 5-2
	Animated Glossary, eTools	Animated Glossary, eTools

Teacher Resource Masters

www.pearsonsuccessnet.com

Topic Start-Up

- Vocabulary Card Sets A–B
- Topic 5 Home-School Connection (English and Spanish)

Topic Wrap-Up

- Topic 5 Test, pages 134–135
- Topic 5 Alternate Assessments, pages 135A–135B

- Reteaching, pages 136–137

MATH STRAND COLORS

● Number and Operations
● Algebra
● Geometry
● Measurement
● Data Analysis and Probability
● Problem Solving

 Lesson 5-3

Using Multiplication to Compare
pp. 114–115

 Lesson 5-4

Writing Multiplication Stories
pp. 116–117

 Lesson 5-5

Problem Solving: Writing to Explain
pp. 118–121

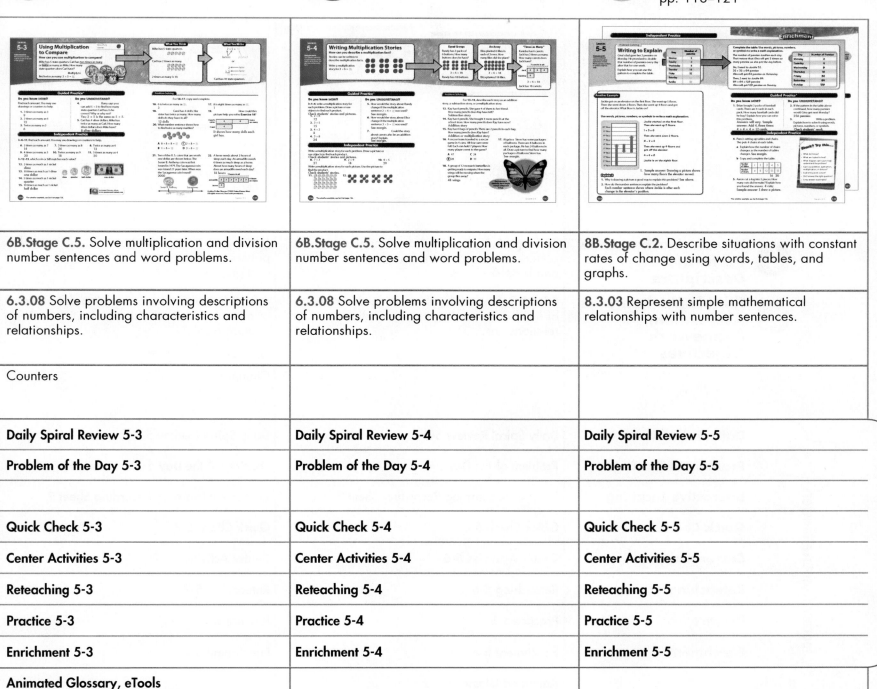

6B.Stage C.5. Solve multiplication and division number sentences and word problems.	**6B.Stage C.5.** Solve multiplication and division number sentences and word problems.	**8B.Stage C.2.** Describe situations with constant rates of change using words, tables, and graphs.
6.3.08 Solve problems involving descriptions of numbers, including characteristics and relationships.	**6.3.08** Solve problems involving descriptions of numbers, including characteristics and relationships.	**8.3.03** Represent simple mathematical relationships with number sentences.
Counters		
Daily Spiral Review 5-3	**Daily Spiral Review 5-4**	**Daily Spiral Review 5-5**
Problem of the Day 5-3	**Problem of the Day 5-4**	**Problem of the Day 5-5**
Quick Check 5-3	**Quick Check 5-4**	**Quick Check 5-5**
Center Activities 5-3	**Center Activities 5-4**	**Center Activities 5-5**
Reteaching 5-3	**Reteaching 5-4**	**Reteaching 5-5**
Practice 5-3	**Practice 5-4**	**Practice 5-5**
Enrichment 5-3	**Enrichment 5-4**	**Enrichment 5-5**
Animated Glossary, eTools		

Lesson 5-6 **2 and 5 as Factors** pp. 122–125

Lesson 5-7 **10 as a Factor** pp. 126–127

	Lesson 5-6	Lesson 5-7
Illinois Mathematics Performance Descriptors	8B.Stage C.1. Represent and analyze simple patterns and operations using words, tables, and graphs.	8B.Stage C.1. Represent and analyze simple patterns and operations using words, tables, and graphs.
Illinois Mathematics Assessment Framework Objectives	6.3.08 Solve problems involving descriptions of numbers, including characteristics and relationships.	6.3.08 Solve problems involving descriptions of numbers, including characteristics and relationships.
		Counters

Teacher Resource Masters

	Lesson 5-6	Lesson 5-7
Daily Spiral Review	Daily Spiral Review 5-6	Daily Spiral Review 5-7
Problem of the Day	Problem of the Day 5-6	Problem of the Day 5-7
Interactive Learning	Interactive Learning Recording Sheet 8	Interactive Learning Recording Sheet 9
Quick Check	Quick Check 5-6	Quick Check 5-7
Center Activities	Center Activities 5-6	Center Activities 5-7
Reteaching	Reteaching 5-6	Reteaching 5-7
Practice	Practice 5-6	Practice 5-7
Enrichment	Enrichment 5-6	Enrichment 5-7

DIGITAL Animated Glossary

www.pearsonsuccessnet.com

Lesson 5-8
9 as a Factor
pp. 128–129

Lesson 5-9
Multiplying with 0 and 1
pp. 130–131

Lesson 5-10
Problem Solving: Two-Question Problems
pp. 132–133

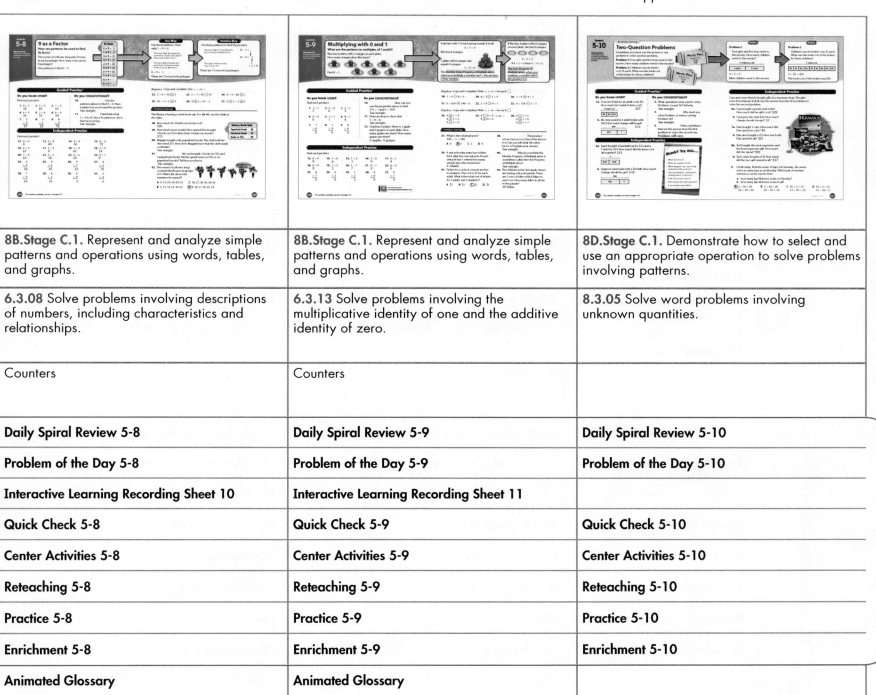

8B.Stage C.1. Represent and analyze simple patterns and operations using words, tables, and graphs.	**8B.Stage C.1.** Represent and analyze simple patterns and operations using words, tables, and graphs.	**8D.Stage C.1.** Demonstrate how to select and use an appropriate operation to solve problems involving patterns.
6.3.08 Solve problems involving descriptions of numbers, including characteristics and relationships.	**6.3.13** Solve problems involving the multiplicative identity of one and the additive identity of zero.	**8.3.05** Solve word problems involving unknown quantities.
Counters	Counters	
Daily Spiral Review 5-8	**Daily Spiral Review 5-9**	**Daily Spiral Review 5-10**
Problem of the Day 5-8	**Problem of the Day 5-9**	**Problem of the Day 5-10**
Interactive Learning Recording Sheet 10	**Interactive Learning Recording Sheet 11**	
Quick Check 5-8	**Quick Check 5-9**	**Quick Check 5-10**
Center Activities 5-8	**Center Activities 5-9**	**Center Activities 5-10**
Reteaching 5-8	**Reteaching 5-9**	**Reteaching 5-10**
Practice 5-8	**Practice 5-9**	**Practice 5-10**
Enrichment 5-8	**Enrichment 5-9**	**Enrichment 5-10**
Animated Glossary	**Animated Glossary**	

Lesson 6-1
3 as a Factor
pp. 140–141

Lesson 6-2
4 as a Factor
pp. 142–143

	Lesson 6-1	**Lesson 6-2**
Illinois Mathematics Performance Descriptors	**6B.Stage C.4.** Demonstrate fluency with basic multiplication and division facts.	**6B.Stage C.4.** Demonstrate fluency with basic multiplication and division facts.
Illinois Mathematics Assessment Framework Objectives	**6.3.08** Solve problems involving descriptions of numbers, including characteristics and relationships (e.g., odd/even, factors/multiples, greater than, less than).	**6.3.08** Solve problems involving descriptions of numbers, including characteristics and relationships (e.g., odd/even, factors/multiples, greater than, less than).
	Counters	Counters

Teacher Resource Masters

Daily Spiral Review	**Daily Spiral Review 6-1**	**Daily Spiral Review 6-2**
Problem of the Day	**Problem of the Day 6-1**	**Problem of the Day 6-2**
Interactive Learning		
Quick Check	**Quick Check 6-1**	**Quick Check 6-2**
Center Activities	**Center Activities 6-1**	**Center Activities 6-2**
Reteaching	**Reteaching 6-1**	**Reteaching 6-2**
Practice	**Practice 6-1**	**Practice 6-2**
Enrichment	**Enrichment 6-1**	**Enrichment 6-2**
DIGITAL	eTools	eTools

www.pearsonsuccessnet.com

Topic Start-Up
- Vocabulary Cards
- Topic 6 Home-School Connection (English and Spanish)

Topic Wrap-Up
- Topic 6 Test, pages 158–159
- Topic 6 Alternate Assessments, pages 159A–159B

- Reteaching, pages 160–161

Lesson 6-3

6 and 7 as Factors
pp. 144–147

Lesson 6-4

8 as a Factor
pp. 148–149

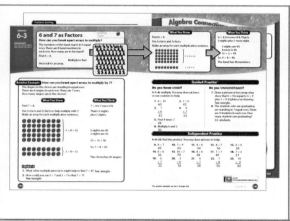

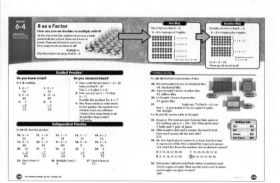

6B.Stage C.4. Demonstrate fluency with basic multiplication and division facts.	**6B.Stage C.4.** Demonstrate fluency with basic multiplication and division facts.
6.3.08 Solve problems involving descriptions of numbers, including characteristics and relationships (e.g., odd/even, factors/multiples, greater than, less than).	**6.3.08** Solve problems involving descriptions of numbers, including characteristics and relationships (e.g., odd/even, factors/multiples, greater than, less than).
Counters	Counters
Daily Spiral Review 6-3	**Daily Spiral Review 6-4**
Problem of the Day 6-3	**Problem of the Day 6-4**
Quick Check 6-3	**Quick Check 6-4**
Center Activities 6-3	**Center Activities 6-4**
Reteaching 6-3	**Reteaching 6-4**
Practice 6-3	**Practice 6-4**
Enrichment 6-3	**Enrichment 6-4**
eTools	

		Lesson 6-5 11 and 12 as Factors pp. 150–151	**Lesson 6-6** Multiplying with 3 Factors pp. 152–153
	Illinois Mathematics Performance Descriptors	6B.Stage C.4. Demonstrate fluency with basic multiplication and division facts.	6B.Stage C.4. Demonstrate fluency with basic multiplication and division facts.
	Illinois Mathematics Assessment Framework Objectives	6.3.08 Solve problems involving descriptions of numbers, including characteristics and relationships (e.g., odd/even, factors/multiples, greater than, less than).	6.3.08 Solve problems involving descriptions of numbers, including characteristics and relationships (e.g., odd/even, factors/multiples, greater than, less than).
			Color Tiles
Teacher Resource Masters	**Daily Spiral Review**	Daily Spiral Review 6-5	Daily Spiral Review 6-6
	Problem of the Day	Problem of the Day 6-5	Problem of the Day 6-6
	Interactive Learning		Interactive Learning Sheet 12
	Quick Check	Quick Check 6-5	Quick Check 6-6
	Center Activities	Center Activities 6-5	Center Activities 6-6
	Reteaching	Reteaching 6-5	Reteaching 6-6
	Practice	Practice 6-5	Practice 6-6
	Enrichment	Enrichment 6-5	Enrichment 6-6
DIGITAL			Animated Glossary

www.pearsonsuccessnet.com

Lesson 6-7

Problem Solving:
Multiple-Step Problems
pp. 154–157

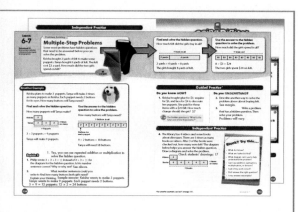

Previews Grade 4: 6B.Stage D.3. Solve multi-step number sentences and word problems using whole numbers and the four basic operations.

8.3.05 Solve word problems involving unknown quantities.

Daily Spiral Review 6-7

Problem of the Day 6-7

Quick Check 6-7

Center Activities 6-7

Reteaching 6-7

Practice 6-7

Enrichment 6-7

Lesson 7-1 Division as Sharing
pp. 164–165

Lesson 7-2 Understanding Remainders
pp. 166–169

	Lesson 7-1 Division as Sharing pp. 164–165	**Lesson 7-2** Understanding Remainders pp. 166–169
Illinois Mathematics Performance Descriptors	6B.Stage C.2. Demonstrate and describe the effects of multiplying and dividing whole numbers using appropriate mathematical notation and vocabulary.	6B.Stage C.2. Demonstrate and describe the effects of multiplying and dividing whole numbers using appropriate mathematical notation and vocabulary.
Illinois Mathematics Assessment Framework Objectives	Previews Grade 5: 6.5.12 Solve problems and number sentences involving addition, subtraction, multiplication, and division using whole numbers.	6.3.08 Solve problems involving descriptions of numbers, including characteristics and relationships (e.g., odd/even, factors/multiples, greater than, less than).
	Counters	Two-color counters

Teacher Resource Masters		
Daily Spiral Review	Daily Spiral Review 7-1	Daily Spiral Review 7-2
Problem of the Day	Problem of the Day 7-1	Problem of the Day 7-2
Interactive Learning	Interactive Learning Recording Sheet 13	
Quick Check	Quick Check 7-1	Quick Check 7-2
Center Activities	Center Activities 7-1	Center Activities 7-2
Reteaching	Reteaching 7-1	Reteaching 7-2
Practice	Practice 7-1	Practice 7-2
Enrichment	Enrichment 7-1	Enrichment 7-2
DIGITAL www.pearsonsuccessnet.com	Animated Glossary, eTools	Animated Glossary

Topic Start-Up
- Vocabulary Cards
- Topic 7 Home-School Connection (English and Spanish)

Topic Wrap-Up
- Topic 7 Test, pages 178–179
- Topic 7 Alternate Assessments, pages 179A–179B

- Reteaching, pages 180–181

MATH STRAND COLORS

- ● Number and Operations
- ● Algebra
- ● Geometry
- ● Measurement
- ● Data Analysis and Probability
- ● Problem Solving

Lesson 7-3
Division as Repeated Subtraction
pp. 170–171

Lesson 7-4
Writing Division Stories
pp. 172–173

Lesson 7-5
Problem Solving: Use Objects and Draw a Picture
pp. 174–177

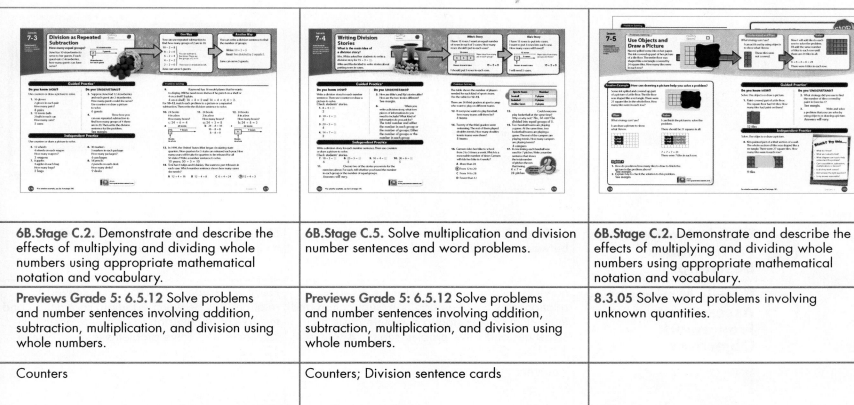

6B.Stage C.2. Demonstrate and describe the effects of multiplying and dividing whole numbers using appropriate mathematical notation and vocabulary.	**6B.Stage C.5.** Solve multiplication and division number sentences and word problems.	**6B.Stage C.2.** Demonstrate and describe the effects of multiplying and dividing whole numbers using appropriate mathematical notation and vocabulary.
Previews Grade 5: 6.5.12 Solve problems and number sentences involving addition, subtraction, multiplication, and division using whole numbers.	**Previews Grade 5: 6.5.12** Solve problems and number sentences involving addition, subtraction, multiplication, and division using whole numbers.	**8.3.05** Solve word problems involving unknown quantities.
Counters	Counters; Division sentence cards	
Daily Spiral Review 7-3	Daily Spiral Review 7-4	Daily Spiral Review 7-5
Problem of the Day 7-3	Problem of the Day 7-4	Problem of the Day 7-5
		Interactive Learning Recording Sheet 14
Quick Check 7-3	Quick Check 7-4	Quick Check 7-5
Center Activities 7-3	Center Activities 7-4	Center Activities 7-5
Reteaching 7-3	Reteaching 7-4	Reteaching 7-5
Practice 7-3	Practice 7-4	Practice 7-5
Enrichment 7-3	Enrichment 7-4	Enrichment 7-5
eTools	eTools	

Lesson
8-1

Relating Multiplication and Division
pp. 184–185

Lesson
8-2

Fact Families with 2, 3, 4, and 5
pp. 186–189

	Lesson 8-1	Lesson 8-2
Illinois Mathematics Performance Descriptors	**6B.Stage C.1.** Show and use the relationship between multiplication and division.	**6B.Stage C.4.** Demonstrate fluency with basic multiplication and division facts.
Illinois Mathematics Assessment Framework Objectives	**Previews Grade 4: 6.4.15** Use the inverse relationships between addition/subtraction and multiplication/division to complete basic fact sentences and solve problems (e.g., $4 \times 3 = 12$, $12 \div 3 = \_\_$).	**Previews Grade 4: 6.4.15** Use the inverse relationships between addition/subtraction and multiplication/division to complete basic fact sentences and solve problems (e.g., $4 \times 3 = 12$, $12 \div 3 = \_\_$).
	Counters	

Teacher Resource Masters

	Lesson 8-1	Lesson 8-2
Daily Spiral Review	Daily Spiral Review 8-1	Daily Spiral Review 8-2
Problem of the Day	Problem of the Day 8-1	Problem of the Day 8-2
Interactive Learning		
Quick Check	Quick Check 8-1	Quick Check 8-2
Center Activities	Center Activities 8-1	Center Activities 8-2
Reteaching	Reteaching 8-1	Reteaching 8-2
Practice	Practice 8-1	Practice 8-2
Enrichment	Enrichment 8-1	Enrichment 8-2

DIGITAL

www.pearsonsuccessnet.com

Animated Glossary, eTools

Topic Start-Up

- Vocabulary Cards
- Topic 8 Home-School Connection (English and Spanish)

Topic Wrap-Up

- Topic 8 Test, pages 200–201
- Topic 8 Alternate Assessments, pages 201A–201B

- Reteaching, pages 202–203
- Cumulative Test Topics 1–8, pages 203A–203B
- Benchmark Test Topics 5–8, pages 203C–203D

MATH STRAND COLORS

● Number and Operations
● Algebra
● Geometry

● Measurement
● Data Analysis and Probability
● Problem Solving

Lesson 8-3

Fact Families with 6 and 7
pp. 190–191

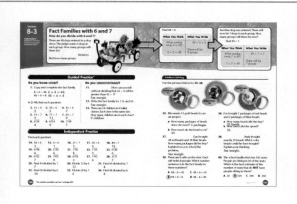

6B.Stage C.4. Demonstrate fluency with basic multiplication and division facts.

Previews Grade 4: 6.4.15 Use the inverse relationships between addition/subtraction and multiplication/division to complete basic fact sentences and solve problems (e.g., $4 \times 3 = 12$, $12 \div 3 = $ __).

Daily Spiral Review 8-3

Problem of the Day 8-3

Quick Check 8-3

Center Activities 8-3

Reteaching 8-3

Practice 8-3

Enrichment 8-3

Lesson 8-4   Fact Families with 8 and 9
pp. 192–193

 Lesson 8-5   Dividing with 0 and 1
pp. 194–195

	Lesson 8-4	Lesson 8-5
Illinois Mathematics Performance Descriptors	6B.Stage C.4. Demonstrate fluency with basic multiplication and division facts.	6B.Stage C.4. Demonstrate fluency with basic multiplication and division facts.
Illinois Mathematics Assessment Framework Objectives	Previews Grade 4: 6.4.15 Use the inverse relationships between addition/subtraction and multiplication/division to complete basic fact sentences and solve problems (e.g., 4 × 3 = 12, 12 ÷ 3 = __).	6.3.13 Solve problems involving the multiplicative identity of one (e.g., 3 × 1 = 3) and the additive identity of zero (e.g., 3 + 0 = 3).
		Counters
Daily Spiral Review	Daily Spiral Review 8-4	Daily Spiral Review 8-5
Problem of the Day	Problem of the Day 8-4	Problem of the Day 8-5
Interactive Learning		
Quick Check	Quick Check 8-4	Quick Check 8-5
Center Activities	Center Activities 8-4	Center Activities 8-5
Reteaching	Reteaching 8-4	Reteaching 8-5
Practice	Practice 8-4	Practice 8-5
Enrichment	Enrichment 8-4	Enrichment 8-5

Teacher Resource Masters

DIGITAL www.pearsonsuccessnet.com

MATH STRAND COLORS

- Number and Operations
- Algebra
- Geometry
- Measurement
- Data Analysis and Probability
- Problem Solving

Lesson 8-6

Problem Solving: Draw a Picture and Write a Number Sentence pp. 196–199

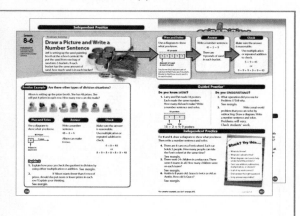

6B.Stage C.5. Solve multiplication and division number sentences and word problems.

8.3.03 Represent simple mathematical relationships with number sentences (equations and inequalities).

Daily Spiral Review 8-6

Problem of the Day 8-6

Quick Check 8-6

Center Activities 8-6

Reteaching 8-6

Practice 8-6

Enrichment 8-6

Lesson 9-1
Repeating Patterns
pp. 206–207

Lesson 9-2
Number Sequences
pp. 208–209

	Repeating Patterns (9-1)	Number Sequences (9-2)
Student Edition Pages		
Illinois Mathematics Performance Descriptors	8A.Stage C.1. Extend geometric and simple numeric patterns using concrete objects or paper and pencil.	8A.Stage C.1. Extend geometric and simple numeric patterns using concrete objects or paper and pencil.
Illinois Mathematics Assessment Framework Objectives	8.3.01 Determine a missing term in a pattern, describe a pattern, and extend a pattern when given a description or pattern.	8.3.01 Determine a missing term in a pattern, describe a pattern, and extend a pattern when given a description or pattern.
Materials	Pattern blocks	
Daily Spiral Review	Daily Spiral Review 9-1	Daily Spiral Review 9-2
Problem of the Day	Problem of the Day 9-1	Problem of the Day 9-2
Interactive Learning		Interactive Learning Recording Sheet 15
Quick Check	Quick Check 9-1	Quick Check 9-2
Center Activities	Center Activities 9-1	Center Activities 9-2
Reteaching	Reteaching 9-1	Reteaching 9-2
Practice	Practice 9-1	Practice 9-2
Enrichment	Enrichment 9-1	Enrichment 9-2
Digital Resources www.pearsonsuccessnet.com	Animated Glossary	

Teacher Resource Masters

Topic Start-Up
- Vocabulary Cards
- Topic 9 Home-School Connection (English and Spanish)

Topic Wrap-Up
- Topic 9 Test, pages 228–229
- Topic 9 Alternate Assessments, pages 229A–229B
- Reteaching, pages 230–231

MATH STRAND COLORS

- ● Number and Operations
- ● Algebra
- ● Geometry
- ● Measurement
- ● Data Analysis and Probability
- ● Problem Solving

Lesson 9-3

Extending Tables
pp. 210–211

Lesson 9-4

Writing Rules for Situations
pp. 212–215

Lesson 9-5

Translating Words to Expressions
pp. 216–217

8B.Stage C.1. Represent and analyze simple patterns and operations using words, tables, and graphs.	**8B.Stage C.2.** Describe situations with constant rates of change using words, tables, and graphs.	**8A.Stage C.5.** Express mathematical relationships using equations.
8.3.01 Determine a missing term in a pattern, describe a pattern, and extend a pattern when given a description or pattern.	**8.3.01** Determine a missing term in a pattern, describe a pattern, and extend a pattern when given a description or pattern.	**8.3.02** Write an expression to represent a given situation.
Counters		
Daily Spiral Review 9-3	Daily Spiral Review 9-4	Daily Spiral Review 9-5
Problem of the Day 9-3	Problem of the Day 9-4	Problem of the Day 9-5
	Interactive Learning Recording Sheet 16	
Quick Check 9-3	Quick Check 9-4	Quick Check 9-5
Center Activities 9-3	Center Activities 9-4	Center Activities 9-5
Reteaching 9-3	Reteaching 9-4	Reteaching 9-5
Practice 9-3	Practice 9-4	Practice 9-5
Enrichment 9-3	Enrichment 9-4	Enrichment 9-5
		Animated Glossary

Lesson 9-6 Geometric Patterns
pp. 218–221

Lesson 9-7 Equal or Unequal
pp. 222–223

	Geometric Patterns	**Equal or Unequal**
Student Edition Pages		
Illinois Mathematics Performance Descriptors	8A.Stage C.1. Extend geometric and simple numeric patterns using concrete objects or paper and pencil.	8A.Stage C.5. Express mathematical relationships using equations.
Illinois Mathematics Assessment Framework Objectives	8.3.01 Determine a missing term in a pattern, describe a pattern, and extend a pattern when given a description or pattern.	8.3.03 Represent simple mathematical relationships with number sentences.
Materials	Base-Ten unit cubes, centimeter-grid paper	Two-color counters
Daily Spiral Review	Daily Spiral Review 9-6	Daily Spiral Review 9-7
Problem of the Day	Problem of the Day 9-6	Problem of the Day 9-7
Interactive Learning		
Quick Check	Quick Check 9-6	Quick Check 9-7
Center Activities	Center Activities 9-6	Center Activities 9-7
Reteaching	Reteaching 9-6	Reteaching 9-7
Practice	Practice 9-6	Practice 9-7
Enrichment	Enrichment 9-6	Enrichment 9-7
Digital Resources www.pearsonsuccessnet.com	eTools	Animated Glossary

Teacher Resource Masters

Lesson 9-8

Problem Solving: Act It Out and Use Reasoning
pp. 224–227

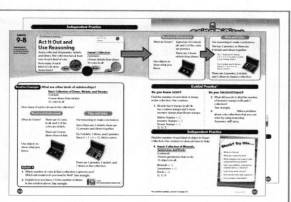

8A.Stage C.5. Express mathematical relationships using equations.

6.3.08 Solve problems involving descriptions of numbers, including characteristics and relationships.

Counters

Daily Spiral Review 9-8

Problem of the Day 9-8

Quick Check 9-8

Center Activities 9-8

Reteaching 9-8

Practice 9-8

Enrichment 9-8

eTools

	Lesson 10-1 Solid Figures pp. 234–237	**Lesson 10-2** Relating Solids and Shapes pp. 238–241
Student Edition Pages		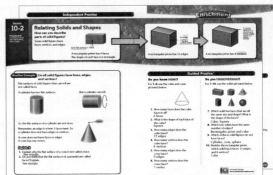
Illinois Mathematics Performance Descriptors	**9B.Stage C.5.** Apply geometric ideas and relationships to problems that arise in the classroom or in everyday life.	**9B.Stage C.1.** Decompose a three-dimensional object into two-dimensional components.
Illinois Mathematics Assessment Framework Objectives	**9.3.02** Identify and describe three-dimensional shapes according to their characteristics.	**9.3.02** Identify and describe three-dimensional shapes according to their characteristics.
Materials	Power solids	Rectangular prism, Net for rectangular prism (Teaching Tool 42)
Daily Spiral Review	Daily Spiral Review 10-1	Daily Spiral Review 10-2
Problem of the Day	Problem of the Day 10-1	Problem of the Day 10-2
Interactive Learning		
Quick Check	Quick Check 10-1	Quick Check 10-2
Center Activities	Center Activities 10-1	Center Activities 10-2
Reteaching	Reteaching 10-1	Reteaching 10-2
Practice	Practice 10-1	Practice 10-2
Enrichment	Enrichment 10-1	Enrichment 10-2
Digital Resources www.pearsonsuccessnet.com	Animated Glossary	Animated Glossary

(Teacher Resource Masters)

Topic Start-Up
- Vocabulary Card Sets A–G
- Topic 10 Home-School Connection (English and Spanish)

Topic Wrap-Up
- Topic 10 Test, pages 254–255
- Topic 10 Alternate Assessments, pages 255A–255B
- Reteaching, pages 256–257

Lesson 10-3 **Lines and Line Segments** pp. 242–243

 Lesson 10-4 **Angles** pp. 244–245

 Lesson 10-5 **Polygons** pp. 246–247

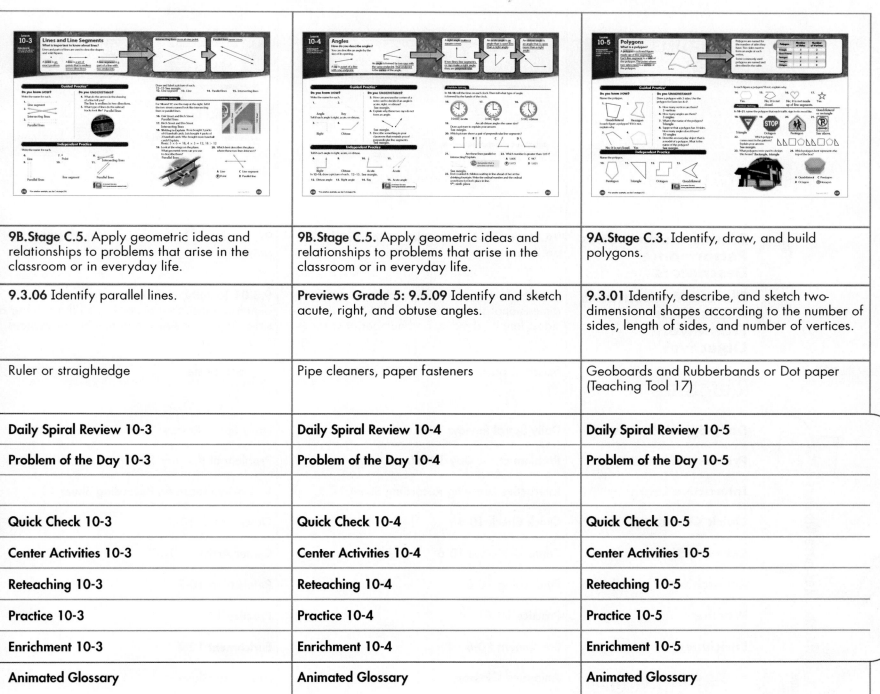

9B.Stage C.5. Apply geometric ideas and relationships to problems that arise in the classroom or in everyday life.	**9B.Stage C.5.** Apply geometric ideas and relationships to problems that arise in the classroom or in everyday life.	**9A.Stage C.3.** Identify, draw, and build polygons.
9.3.06 Identify parallel lines.	**Previews Grade 5: 9.5.09** Identify and sketch acute, right, and obtuse angles.	**9.3.01** Identify, describe, and sketch two-dimensional shapes according to the number of sides, length of sides, and number of vertices.
Ruler or straightedge	Pipe cleaners, paper fasteners	Geoboards and Rubberbands or Dot paper (Teaching Tool 17)
Daily Spiral Review 10-3	**Daily Spiral Review 10-4**	**Daily Spiral Review 10-5**
Problem of the Day 10-3	**Problem of the Day 10-4**	**Problem of the Day 10-5**
Quick Check 10-3	**Quick Check 10-4**	**Quick Check 10-5**
Center Activities 10-3	**Center Activities 10-4**	**Center Activities 10-5**
Reteaching 10-3	**Reteaching 10-4**	**Reteaching 10-5**
Practice 10-3	**Practice 10-4**	**Practice 10-5**
Enrichment 10-3	**Enrichment 10-4**	**Enrichment 10-5**
Animated Glossary	**Animated Glossary**	**Animated Glossary**

	Lesson 10-6 — **Triangles** pp. 248–249	Lesson 10-7 — **Quadrilaterals** pp. 250–251
Student Edition Pages		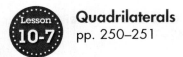
Illinois Mathematics Performance Descriptors	9A.Stage C.3. Identify, draw, and build polygons.	9A.Stage C.3. Identify, draw, and build polygons.
Illinois Mathematics Assessment Framework Objectives	9.3.01 Identify, describe, and sketch two-dimensional shapes according to the number of sides, length of sides, and number of vertices.	9.3.01 Identify, describe, and sketch two-dimensional shapes according to the number of sides, length of sides, and number of vertices.
Materials	Scissors, paste	Scissors, paste
Daily Spiral Review	Daily Spiral Review 10-6	Daily Spiral Review 10-7
Problem of the Day	Problem of the Day 10-6	Problem of the Day 10-7
Interactive Learning	Interactive Learning Recording Sheet 17	Interactive Learning Recording Sheet 18
Quick Check	Quick Check 10-6	Quick Check 10-7
Center Activities	Center Activities 10-6	Center Activities 10-7
Reteaching	Reteaching 10-6	Reteaching 10-7
Practice	Practice 10-6	Practice 10-7
Enrichment	Enrichment 10-6	Enrichment 10-7
Digital Resources www.pearsonsuccessnet.com	Animated Glossary	Animated Glossary

Teacher Resource Masters

Lesson 10-8

Problem Solving:
Make and Test Generalizations
pp. 252–253

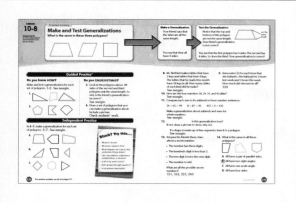

9C.Stage C.1. Make and test conjectures about mathematical properties and relationships and justify the conclusions.

9.3.01 Identify, describe, and sketch two-dimensional shapes according to the number of sides, length of sides, and number of vertices.

Daily Spiral Review 10-8

Problem of the Day 10-8

Quick Check 10-8

Center Activities 10-8

Reteaching 10-8

Practice 10-8

Enrichment 10-8

Animated Glossary

Lesson 11-1 Congruent Figures and Motion
pp. 260–263

 Lesson 11-2 Line Symmetry
pp. 264–265

	Lesson 11-1	Lesson 11-2
Student Edition Pages	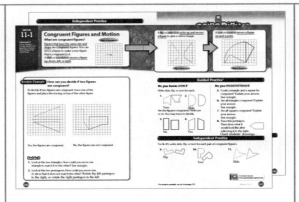	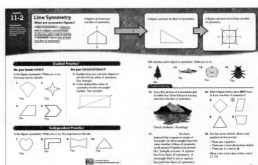
Illinois Mathematics Performance Descriptors	**9B.Stage C.3.** Describe a motion or a series of motions that will show that two shapes are congruent.	**9A.Stage C.3.** Identify, draw, and build polygons.
Illinois Mathematics Assessment Framework Objectives	**9.3.10** Identify congruent and similar figures by visual inspection.	**9.3.04** Identify whether or not a figure has a line of symmetry, and sketch or identify the line of symmetry.
Materials	Geoboards, rubberbands, dot paper (Teaching Tool 17)	Scissors, paste
Daily Spiral Review	Daily Spiral Review 11-1	Daily Spiral Review 11-2
Problem of the Day	Problem of the Day 11-1	Problem of the Day 11-2
Interactive Learning		Interactive Learning Recording Sheet 19
Quick Check	Quick Check 11-1	Quick Check 11-2
Center Activities	Center Activities 11-1	Center Activities 11-2
Reteaching	Reteaching 11-1	Reteaching 11-2
Practice	Practice 11-1	Practice 11-2
Enrichment	Enrichment 11-1	Enrichment 11-2
Digital Resources www.pearsonsuccessnet.com	Animated Glossary, eTools	Animated Glossary, eTools

Teacher Resource Masters

Topic Start-Up

- Vocabulary Card Sets A–B
- Topic 11 Home-School Connection (English and Spanish)

Topic Wrap-Up

- Topic 11 Test, pages 270–271
- Topic 11 Alternate Assessments, pages 271A–271B
- Reteaching, pages 272–273

MATH STRAND COLORS

● Number and Operations   ● Measurement
● Algebra   ● Data Analysis and Probability
● Geometry   ● Problem Solving

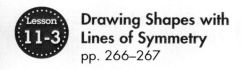

Lesson 11-3
Drawing Shapes with Lines of Symmetry
pp. 266–267

Lesson 11-4
Problem Solving: Use Objects
pp. 268–269

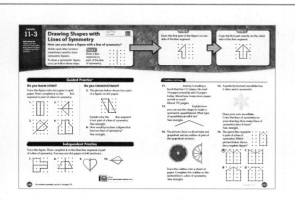 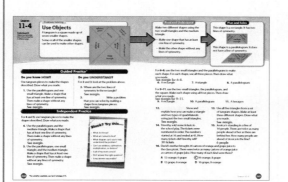

9A.Stage C.3. Identify, draw, and build polygons.	**9A.Stage C.3.** Identify, draw, and build polygons.
9.3.04 Identify whether or not a figure has a line of symmetry, and sketch or identify the line of symmetry.	**9.3.09** Predict the result of putting shapes together (composing) and taking them apart (decomposing).
Dot paper (Teaching Tool 17)	Tangram pieces (Teaching Tool 37), scissors
Daily Spiral Review 11-3	**Daily Spiral Review 11-4**
Problem of the Day 11-3	**Problem of the Day 11-4**
Quick Check 11-3	**Quick Check 11-4**
Center Activities 11-3	**Center Activities 11-4**
Reteaching 11-3	**Reteaching 11-4**
Practice 11-3	**Practice 11-4**
Enrichment 11-3	**Enrichment 11-4**
eTools	**eTools**

Understanding Fractions
ILLINOIS TOPIC PLANNER
Pacing: 1 lesson per day

		Lesson 12-1 Dividing Regions into Equal Parts pp. 276–277	**Lesson 12-2** Fractions and Regions pp. 278–279
	Illinois Mathematics Performance Descriptors	Previews Grade 4: 6A.Stage D.4. Represent fractions as parts of unit wholes, as parts of a set, as locations on a number line, and as divisions of whole numbers.	Previews Grade 4: 6A.Stage D.4. Represent fractions as parts of unit wholes, as parts of a set, as locations on a number line, and as divisions of whole numbers.
	Illinois Mathematics Assessment Framework Objectives	Previews Grade 4: 6.4.03 Read, write, recognize, and model equivalent representations of fractions; divide regions or sets to represent a fraction.	6.3.03 Recognize a fraction represented with a pictorial model.
		Centimeter-grid paper	
Teacher Resource Masters	**Daily Spiral Review**	Daily Spiral Review 12-1	Daily Spiral Review 12-2
	Problem of the Day	Problem of the Day 12-1	Problem of the Day 12-2
	Interactive Learning		Interactive Learning Recording Sheet 20
	Quick Check	Quick Check 12-1	Quick Check 12-2
	Center Activities	Center Activities 12-1	Center Activities 12-2
	Reteaching	Reteaching 12-1	Reteaching 12-2
	Practice	Practice 12-1	Practice 12-2
	Enrichment	Enrichment 12-1	Enrichment 12-2
DIGITAL www.pearsonsuccessnet.com		Animated Glossary	Animated Glossary

Topic Start-Up
- Vocabulary Card Sets A–C
- Topic 12 Home-School Connection (English and Spanish)

Topic Wrap-Up
- Topic 12 Test, pages 300–301
- Topic 12 Alternate Assessments, pages 301A–301B

- Reteaching, pages 302–303
- Cumulative Test Topics 1–12, pages 303A–303B
- Benchmark Test Topics 9–12, pages 303C–303D

MATH STRAND COLORS

- Number and Operations
- Algebra
- Geometry
- Measurement
- Data Analysis and Probability
- Problem Solving

Lesson 12-3
Fractions and Sets
pp. 280–281

Lesson 12-4
Benchmark Fractions
pp. 282–283

Lesson 12-5
Finding Equivalent Fractions
pp. 284–287

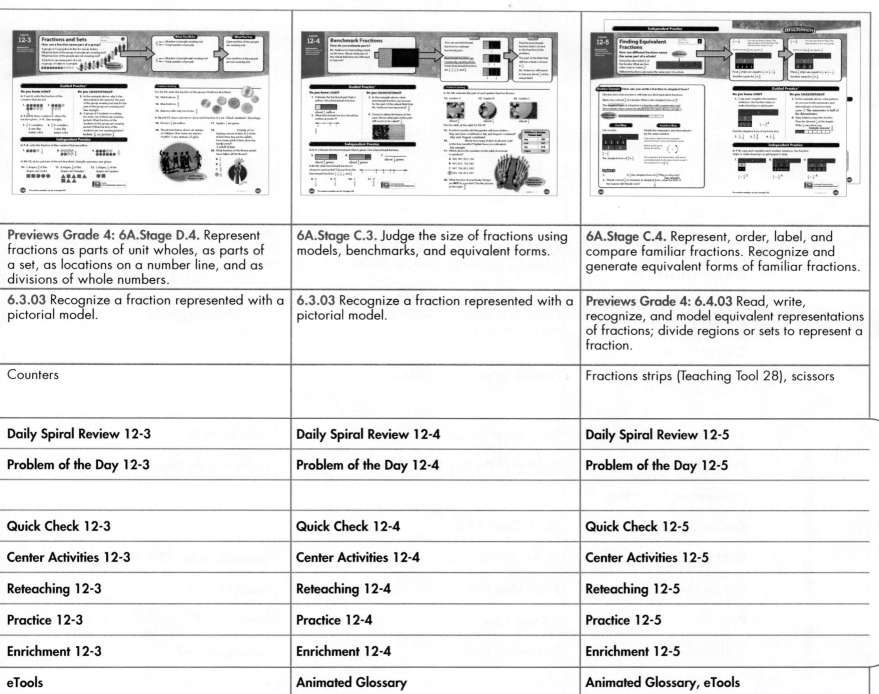

Previews Grade 4: 6A.Stage D.4. Represent fractions as parts of unit wholes, as parts of a set, as locations on a number line, and as divisions of whole numbers.	6A.Stage C.3. Judge the size of fractions using models, benchmarks, and equivalent forms.	6A.Stage C.4. Represent, order, label, and compare familiar fractions. Recognize and generate equivalent forms of familiar fractions.
6.3.03 Recognize a fraction represented with a pictorial model.	6.3.03 Recognize a fraction represented with a pictorial model.	Previews Grade 4: 6.4.03 Read, write, recognize, and model equivalent representations of fractions; divide regions or sets to represent a fraction.
Counters		Fractions strips (Teaching Tool 28), scissors
Daily Spiral Review 12-3	Daily Spiral Review 12-4	Daily Spiral Review 12-5
Problem of the Day 12-3	Problem of the Day 12-4	Problem of the Day 12-5
Quick Check 12-3	Quick Check 12-4	Quick Check 12-5
Center Activities 12-3	Center Activities 12-4	Center Activities 12-5
Reteaching 12-3	Reteaching 12-4	Reteaching 12-5
Practice 12-3	Practice 12-4	Practice 12-5
Enrichment 12-3	Enrichment 12-4	Enrichment 12-5
eTools	Animated Glossary	Animated Glossary, eTools

Understanding Fractions
ILLINOIS TOPIC PLANNER   Pacing: 1 lesson per day

		Lesson 12-6 — Using Models to Compare Fractions pp. 288–289	Lesson 12-7 — Fractions on the Number Line pp. 290–293
	Illinois Mathematics Performance Descriptors	6A.Stage C.4. Represent, order, label, and compare familiar fractions. Recognize and generate equivalent forms of familiar fractions.	Previews Grade 4: 6A.Stage D.4. Represent fractions as parts of unit wholes, as parts of a set, as locations on a number line, and as divisions of whole numbers.
	Illinois Mathematics Assessment Framework Objectives	Previews Grade 4: 6.4.07 Order and compare fractions having like denominators with or without models.	Previews Grade 4: 6.4.08 Identify and locate whole numbers, halves, and fourths on a number line.
		Fraction strips (Teaching Tool 28)	
Teacher Resource Masters	**Daily Spiral Review**	Daily Spiral Review 12-6	Daily Spiral Review 12-7
	Problem of the Day	Problem of the Day 12-6	Problem of the Day 12-7
	Interactive Learning		
	Quick Check	Quick Check 12-6	Quick Check 12-7
	Center Activities	Center Activities 12-6	Center Activities 12-7
	Reteaching	Reteaching 12-6	Reteaching 12-7
	Practice	Practice 12-6	Practice 12-7
	Enrichment	Enrichment 12-6	Enrichment 12-7
DIGITAL www.pearsonsuccessnet.com		eTools	Animated Glossary

Lesson 12-8
Using Models to Add Fractions
pp. 294–295

 Lesson 12-9
Using Models to Subtract Fractions
pp. 296–297

 Lesson 12-10
Problem Solving: Make a Table and Look for a Pattern
pp. 298–299

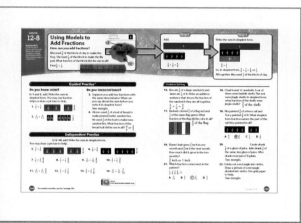

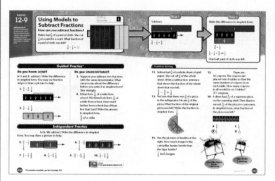

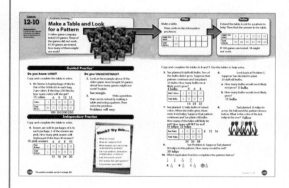

Previews Grade 4: 6B.Stage D.2. Solve addition or subtraction number sentences and word problems using fractions with like denominators.	Previews Grade 4: 6B.Stage D.2. Solve addition or subtraction number sentences and word problems using fractions with like denominators.	8B.Stage C.1. Represent and analyze simple patterns and operations using words, tables, and graphs.
Previews Grade 4: 6.4.13 Model situations involving addition and subtraction of fractions with like denominators.	Previews Grade 4: 6.4.13 Model situations involving addition and subtraction of fractions with like denominators.	8.3.01 Determine a missing term in a pattern (sequence), describe a pattern (sequence), and extend a pattern (sequence) when given a description or pattern (sequence).
Fraction strips (Teaching Tool 28)	Fraction strips (Teaching Tool 28)	
Daily Spiral Review 12-8	Daily Spiral Review 12-9	Daily Spiral Review 12-10
Problem of the Day 12-8	Problem of the Day 12-9	Problem of the Day 12-10
Quick Check 12-8	Quick Check 12-9	Quick Check 12-10
Center Activities 12-8	Center Activities 12-9	Center Activities 12-10
Reteaching 12-8	Reteaching 12-9	Reteaching 12-10
Practice 12-8	Practice 12-9	Practice 12-10
Enrichment 12-8	Enrichment 12-9	Enrichment 12-10
eTools	eTools	

Lesson 13-1
Fractions and Decimals
pp. 306–307

Lesson 13-2
Using Money to Understand Decimals
pp. 308–311

	Lesson 13-1	Lesson 13-2
Illinois Mathematics Performance Descriptors	6A.Stage C.4. Represent, order, label, and compare familiar fractions. Recognize and generate equivalent forms of familiar fractions.	6A.Stage C.5. Explore and discuss uses of decimals.
Illinois Mathematics Assessment Framework Objectives	6.3.03 Recognize a fraction represented with a pictorial model.	6.3.06 Order and compare decimals expressed using monetary units.
	Decimal models (Teaching Tool 31), crayons or markers	Bills and Coins (Teaching Tool 36), scissors

Teacher Resource Masters		
Daily Spiral Review	Daily Spiral Review 13-1	Daily Spiral Review 13-2
Problem of the Day	Problem of the Day 13-1	Problem of the Day 13-2
Interactive Learning		
Quick Check	Quick Check 13-1	Quick Check 13-2
Center Activities	Center Activities 13-1	Center Activities 13-2
Reteaching	Reteaching 13-1	Reteaching 13-2
Practice	Practice 13-1	Practice 13-2
Enrichment	Enrichment 13-1	Enrichment 13-2
DIGITAL www.pearsonsuccessnet.com	Animated Glossary	eTools

Topic Start-Up

- Vocabulary Cards
- Topic 13 Home-School Connection (English and Spanish)

Topic Wrap-Up

- Topic 13 Test, pages 322–323
- Topic 13 Alternate Assessments, pages 323A–323B

- Reteaching, pages 324–325

MATH STRAND COLORS

- Number and Operations
- Algebra
- Geometry
- Measurement
- Data Analysis and Probability
- Problem Solving

Lesson 13-3

Adding and Subtracting Money
pp. 312–315

Lesson 13-4

Problem Solving: Draw a Picture and Write a Number Sentence pp. 316–319

Lesson 13-5

Problem Solving: Missing or Extra Information
pp. 320–321

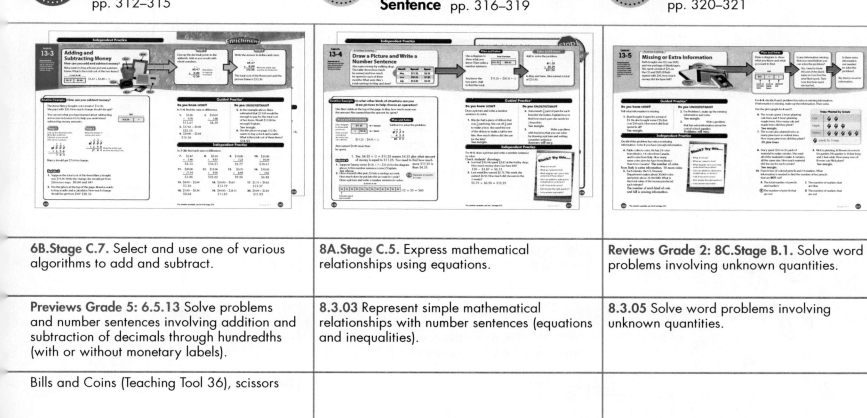

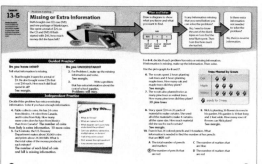

6B.Stage C.7. Select and use one of various algorithms to add and subtract.	**8A.Stage C.5.** Express mathematical relationships using equations.	**Reviews Grade 2: 8C.Stage B.1.** Solve word problems involving unknown quantities.
Previews Grade 5: 6.5.13 Solve problems and number sentences involving addition and subtraction of decimals through hundredths (with or without monetary labels).	**8.3.03** Represent simple mathematical relationships with number sentences (equations and inequalities).	**8.3.05** Solve word problems involving unknown quantities.
Bills and Coins (Teaching Tool 36), scissors		
Daily Spiral Review 13-3	**Daily Spiral Review 13-4**	**Daily Spiral Review 13-5**
Problem of the Day 13-3	**Problem of the Day 13-4**	**Problem of the Day 13-5**
Quick Check 13-3	**Quick Check 13-4**	**Quick Check 13-5**
Center Activities 13-3	**Center Activities 13-4**	**Center Activities 13-5**
Reteaching 13-3	**Reteaching 13-4**	**Reteaching 13-5**
Practice 13-3	**Practice 13-4**	**Practice 13-5**
Enrichment 13-3	**Enrichment 13-4**	**Enrichment 13-5**

Customary Measurement
ILLINOIS TOPIC PLANNER
Pacing: 1 lesson per day

 Lesson 14-1 Understanding Measurement pp. 328–331

 Lesson 14-2 Fractions of an Inch pp. 332–333

	Lesson 14-1	Lesson 14-2
Student Edition Pages	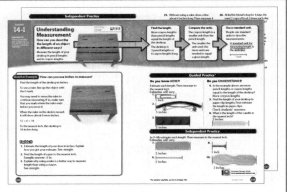	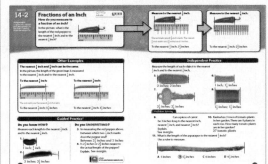
Illinois Mathematics Performance Descriptors	7A.Stage C.2. Measure objects using standard units in the U.S. customary and metric systems.	7A.Stage C.2. Measure objects using standard units in the U.S. customary and metric systems.
Illinois Mathematics Assessment Framework Objectives	7.3.02 Select and use appropriate standard units and tools to measure length (to the nearest inch or cm), time (to the nearest minute), and temperature (to the nearest degree).	7.3.02 Select and use appropriate standard units and tools to measure length (to the nearest inch or cm), time (to the nearest minute), and temperature (to the nearest degree).
Materials	Inch ruler	Inch ruler
Daily Spiral Review	Daily Spiral Review 14-1	Daily Spiral Review 14-2
Problem of the Day	Problem of the Day 14-1	Problem of the Day 14-2
Interactive Learning		Interactive Learning Recording Sheet 21
Quick Check	Quick Check 14-1	Quick Check 14-2
Center Activities	Center Activities 14-1	Center Activities 14-2
Reteaching	Reteaching 14-1	Reteaching 14-2
Practice	Practice 14-1	Practice 14-2
Enrichment	Enrichment 14-1	Enrichment 14-2
Digital Resources www.pearsonsuccessnet.com	Animated Glossary, eTools	eTools

Teacher Resource Masters

Topic Start-Up
- Vocabulary Card Sets A–C
- Topic 14 Home-School Connection (English and Spanish)

Topic Wrap-Up
- Topic 14 Test, pages 344–345
- Topic 14 Alternate Assessments, pages 345A–345B

- Reteaching, pages 346–347

MATH STRAND COLORS

● Number and Operations   ● Measurement
● Algebra   ● Data Analysis and Probability
● Geometry   ● Problem Solving

Lesson 14-3

Using Inches, Feet, Yards, and Miles
pp. 334–337

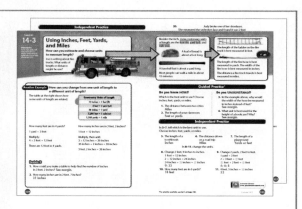

7A.Stage C.3. Perform simple unit conversions within a system of measurement (e.g., three feet is the same as a yard).

7.3.07 Solve problems involving simple unit conversions <u>within the same measurement system</u> for time and length.

Yardstick

Daily Spiral Review 14-3

Problem of the Day 14-3

Interactive Learning Recording Sheet 22

Quick Check 14-3

Center Activities 14-3

Reteaching 14-3

Practice 14-3

Enrichment 14-3

Animated Glossary

	Lesson 14-4 Customary Units of Capacity pp. 338–339	**Lesson 14-5** Units of Weight pp. 340–341
Student Edition Pages		
Illinois Mathematics Performance Descriptors	**7C.Stage C.1.** Select and apply appropriate standard units and tools to measure length, area, volume, weight, time, and temperature.	**7C.Stage C.1.** Select and apply appropriate standard units and tools to measure length, area, volume, weight, time, and temperature.
Illinois Mathematics Assessment Framework Objectives	Previews Grade 5: **7.5.02** Select and use appropriate standard units and tools to measure length (to the nearest $\frac{1}{4}$ inch or mm), mass/weight, capacity, and angles.	**7.3.05** Compare and estimate length (including perimeter), area, and weight/mass using referents.
Materials		Pan balance
Daily Spiral Review	Daily Spiral Review 14-4	Daily Spiral Review 14-5
Problem of the Day	Problem of the Day 14-4	Problem of the Day 14-5
Interactive Learning	Interactive Learning Recording Sheet 23	
Quick Check	Quick Check 14-4	Quick Check 14-5
Center Activities	Center Activities 14-4	Center Activities 14-5
Reteaching	Reteaching 14-4	Reteaching 14-5
Practice	Practice 14-4	Practice 14-5
Enrichment	Enrichment 14-4	Enrichment 14-5
Digital Resources www.pearsonsuccessnet.com	Animated Glossary	Animated Glossary

Teacher Resource Masters

Lesson 14-6

Problem Solving:
Act It Out and Use Reasoning
pp. 342–343

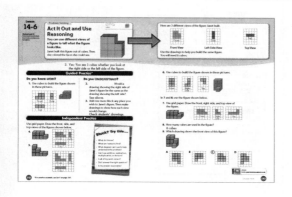

9B.Stage C.1. Decompose a three-dimensional object into two-dimensional components.

9.3.02 Identify and describe three-dimensional shapes (cubes, spheres, cones, cylinders, prisms, and pyramids) according to their characteristics (faces, edges, vertices).

Unit cubes

Daily Spiral Review 14-6

Problem of the Day 14-6

Quick Check 14-6

Center Activities 14-6

Reteaching 14-6

Practice 14-6

Enrichment 14-6

eTools

	Lesson 15-1 Using Centimeters and Decimeters pp. 350–351	**Lesson 15-2** Using Meters and Kilometers pp. 352–355
Student Edition Pages	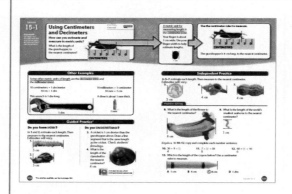	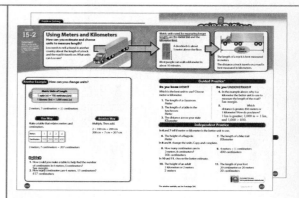
Illinois Mathematics Performance Descriptors	7A.Stage C.2. Measure objects using standard units in the U.S. customary and metric systems.	7A.Stage C.3. Perform simple unit conversions within a system of measurement (e.g., three feet is the same as a yard).
Illinois Mathematics Assessment Framework Objectives	7.3.02 Select and use appropriate standard units and tools to measure length (to the nearest inch or cm), time (to the nearest minute), and temperature (to the nearest degree).	7.3.07 Solve problems involving simple unit conversions within the same measurement system for time and length.
Materials	Centimeter ruler	Meter stick
Daily Spiral Review	Daily Spiral Review 15-1	Daily Spiral Review 15-2
Problem of the Day	Problem of the Day 15-1	Problem of the Day 15-2
Interactive Learning		
Quick Check	Quick Check 15-1	Quick Check 15-2
Center Activities	Center Activities 15-1	Center Activities 15-2
Reteaching	Reteaching 15-1	Reteaching 15-2
Practice	Practice 15-1	Practice 15-2
Enrichment	Enrichment 15-1	Enrichment 15-2
Digital Resources www.pearsonsuccessnet.com	Animated Glossary, eTools	Animated Glossary

Teacher Resource Masters

Topic Start-Up
- Vocabulary Card Sets A–B
- Topic 15 Home-School Connection (English and Spanish)

Topic Wrap-Up
- Topic 15 Test, pages 362–363
- Topic 15 Alternate Assessments, pages 363A–363B

- Reteaching, pages 364–365

MATH STRAND COLORS

● Number and Operations   ● Measurement
● Algebra   ● Data Analysis and Probability
● Geometry   ● Problem Solving

Lesson 15-3
Metric Units of Capacity
pp. 356–357

Lesson 15-4
Units of Mass
pp. 358–359

Lesson 15-5
Problem Solving: Make a Table and Look for a Pattern
pp. 360–361

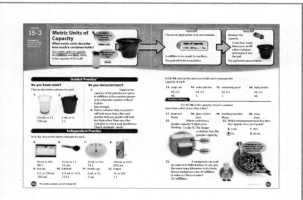

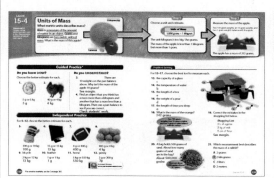

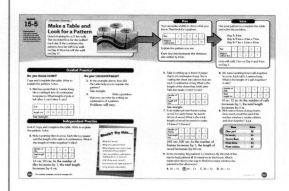

7C.Stage C.1. Select and apply appropriate standard units and tools to measure length, area, volume, weight, time, and temperature.	**7C.Stage C.1.** Select and apply appropriate standard units and tools to measure length, area, volume, weight, time, and temperature.	**8B.Stage C.1.** Represent and analyze simple patterns and operations using words, tables, and graphs.
Previews Grade 5: 7.5.02 Select and use appropriate standard units and tools to measure length (to the nearest $\frac{1}{4}$ inch or mm), mass/weight, capacity, and angles.	**7.3.05** Compare and estimate length (including perimeter), area, and weight/mass using referents.	**8.3.01** Determine a missing term in a pattern (sequence), describe a pattern (sequence), and extend a pattern (sequence) when given a description or pattern (sequence).
Daily Spiral Review 15-3	Daily Spiral Review 15-4	Daily Spiral Review 15-5
Problem of the Day 15-3	Problem of the Day 15-4	Problem of the Day 15-5
Quick Check 15-3	Quick Check 15-4	Quick Check 15-5
Center Activities 15-3	Center Activities 15-4	Center Activities 15-5
Reteaching 15-3	Reteaching 15-4	Reteaching 15-5
Practice 15-3	Practice 15-4	Practice 15-5
Enrichment 15-3	Enrichment 15-4	Enrichment 15-5
Animated Glossary	Animated Glossary	

	Lesson 16-1 **Understanding Perimeter** pp. 368–369	Lesson 16-2 **Perimeter of Common Shapes** pp. 370–371
Student Edition Pages		
Illinois Mathematics Performance Descriptors	7A.Stage C.5. Show and explain perimeter of an object by measuring and adding its linear units.	7A.Stage C.5. Show and explain perimeter of an object by measuring and adding its linear units.
Illinois Mathematics Assessment Framework Objectives	7.3.03 Solve problems involving the perimeter of a polygon with given side lengths or a given non-standard unit (e.g., paperclip).	7.3.03 Solve problems involving the perimeter of a polygon with given side lengths or a given non-standard unit (e.g., paperclip).
Materials	Centimeter-grid paper	Inch ruler
Daily Spiral Review	Daily Spiral Review 16-1	Daily Spiral Review 16-2
Problem of the Day	Problem of the Day 16-1	Problem of the Day 16-2
Interactive Learning		Interactive Learning Recording Sheet 24
Quick Check	Quick Check 16-1	Quick Check 16-2
Center Activities	Center Activities 16-1	Center Activities 16-2
Reteaching	Reteaching 16-1	Reteaching 16-2
Practice	Practice 16-1	Practice 16-2
Enrichment	Enrichment 16-1	Enrichment 16-2
Digital Resources www.pearsonsuccessnet.com	Animated Glossary	

Teacher Resource Masters

Topic Start-Up

- Vocabulary Cards
- Topic 16 Home-School Connection (English and Spanish)

Topic Wrap-Up

- Topic 16 Test, pages 386–387
- Topic 16 Alternate Assessments, pages 387A–387B

- Reteaching, pages 388–389
- Cumulative Test Topics 1–16, pages 389A–389B
- Benchmark Test Topics 13–16, pages 389C–389D

MATH STRAND COLORS

- ● Number and Operations
- ● Algebra
- ● Geometry
- ● Measurement
- ● Data Analysis and Probability
- ● Problem Solving

Lesson 16-3 Different Shapes with the Same Perimeter
pp. 372–373

Lesson 16-4 Problem Solving: Try, Check, and Revise
pp. 374–375

Lesson 16-5 Understanding Area
pp. 376–377

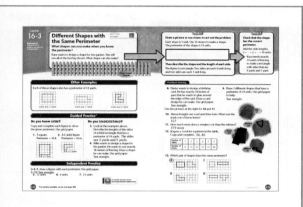

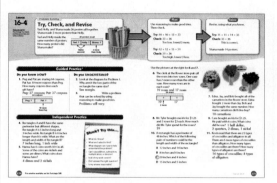

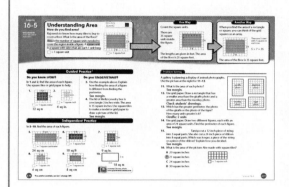

Previews Grade 4: 7C.Stage D.3. Create an accurate representation of a polygon with a given perimeter or area.	8A.Stage C.5. Express mathematical relationships using equations.	7A.Stage C.6. Show and explain the area of an object by counting square units.
7.3.03 Solve problems involving the perimeter of a polygon with given side lengths or a given non-standard unit (e.g., paperclip).	8.3.05 Solve word problems involving unknown quantities.	7.3.04 Solve problems involving the area of a figure when whole and half square units are shown within the figure.
Centimeter-grid paper, straws, craft sticks, or toothpicks	Colored chalk	1-inch grid paper, scissors
Daily Spiral Review 16-3	Daily Spiral Review 16-4	Daily Spiral Review 16-5
Problem of the Day 16-3	Problem of the Day 16-4	Problem of the Day 16-5
		Interactive Learning Recording Sheet 25
Quick Check 16-3	Quick Check 16-4	Quick Check 16-5
Center Activities 16-3	Center Activities 16-4	Center Activities 16-5
Reteaching 16-3	Reteaching 16-4	Reteaching 16-5
Practice 16-3	Practice 16-4	Practice 16-5
Enrichment 16-3	Enrichment 16-4	Enrichment 16-5
Animated Glossary, eTools		Animated Glossary

Lesson 16-6 Estimating and Measuring Area
pp. 378–379

Lesson 16-7 Volume
pp. 380–383

	Lesson 16-6	**Lesson 16-7**
Student Edition Pages		
Illinois Mathematics Performance Descriptors	Previews Grade 4: 7B.Stage D.1. Develop and discuss strategies for estimating the perimeters, areas, and volumes of regular and nonregular shapes.	Previews Grade 4: 7C.Stage D.2. Determine the volume of a cube or rectangular prism using concrete materials.
Illinois Mathematics Assessment Framework Objectives	7.3.05 Compare and estimate length (including perimeter), area, and weight/mass using referents.	7.3.06 Determine the volume of a solid figure that shows cubic units.
Materials		Unit cubes
Daily Spiral Review	Daily Spiral Review 16-6	Daily Spiral Review 16-7
Problem of the Day	Problem of the Day 16-6	Problem of the Day 16-7
Interactive Learning	Interactive Learning Recording Sheet 26	
Quick Check	Quick Check 16-6	Quick Check 16-7
Center Activities	Center Activities 16-6	Center Activities 16-7
Reteaching	Reteaching 16-6	Reteaching 16-7
Practice	Practice 16-6	Practice 16-7
Enrichment	Enrichment 16-6	Enrichment 16-7
Digital Resources www.pearsonsuccessnet.com		Animated Glossary, eTools

Teacher Resource Masters

MATH STRAND COLORS

● Number and Operations   ● Measurement
● Algebra   ● Data Analysis and Probability
● Geometry   ● Problem Solving

Lesson 16-8

Problem Solving:
Solve a Simpler Problem
pp. 384–385

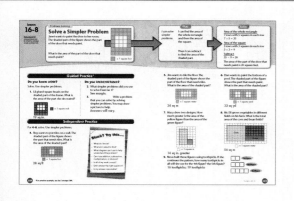

7C.Stage C.3. Solve problems using perimeter and area of simple polygons.

7.3.04 Solve problems involving the area of a figure when whole and half square units are shown within the figure.

Centimeter-grid paper

Daily Spiral Review 16-8

Problem of the Day 16-8

Quick Check 16-8

Center Activities 16-8

Reteaching 16-8

Practice 16-8

Enrichment 16-8

Lesson 17-1 Time to the Half Hour and Quarter Hour
pp. 392–395

Lesson 17-2 Time to the Minute
pp. 396–397

	Time to the Half Hour and Quarter Hour	**Time to the Minute**
Student Edition Pages	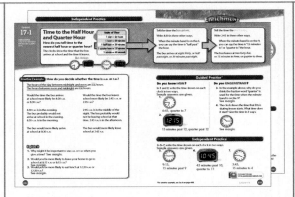	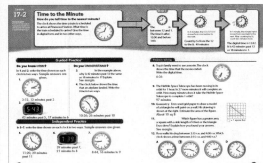
Illinois Mathematics Performance Descriptors	7C.Stage C.1. Select and apply appropriate standard units and tools to measure length, area, volume, weight, time, and temperature.	7C.Stage C.1. Select and apply appropriate standard units and tools to measure length, area, volume, weight, time, and temperature.
Illinois Mathematics Assessment Framework Objectives	7.3.02 Select and use appropriate standard units and tools to measure length (to the nearest inch or cm), time (to the nearest minute), and temperature (to the nearest degree).	7.3.02 Select and use appropriate standard units and tools to measure length (to the nearest inch or cm), time (to the nearest minute), and temperature (to the nearest degree).
Materials	Blank clock faces (Teaching Tool 34), pupil's clock face	Blank clock faces (Teaching Tool 34), pupil's clock face
Daily Spiral Review	**Daily Spiral Review 17-1**	**Daily Spiral Review 17-2**
Problem of the Day	**Problem of the Day 17-1**	**Problem of the Day 17-2**
Interactive Learning		
Quick Check	**Quick Check 17-1**	**Quick Check 17-2**
Center Activities	**Center Activities 17-1**	**Center Activities 17-2**
Reteaching	**Reteaching 17-1**	**Reteaching 17-2**
Practice	**Practice 17-1**	**Practice 17-2**
Enrichment	**Enrichment 17-1**	**Enrichment 17-2**
Digital Resources www.pearsonsuccessnet.com	**Animated Glossary**	

Teacher Resource Masters

Topic Start-Up

- Vocabulary Card Sets A–B
- Topic 17 Home-School Connection (English and Spanish)

Topic Wrap-Up

- Topic 17 Test, pages 406–407
- Topic 17 Alternate Assessments, page 407A–407B

- Reteaching, pages 408–409

MATH STRAND COLORS

- Number and Operations
- Algebra
- Geometry
- Measurement
- Data Analysis and Probability
- Problem Solving

Units of Time
pp. 398–399

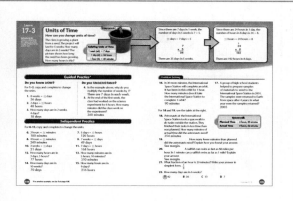

7A.Stage C.3. Perform simple unit conversions within a system of measurement (e.g., three feet is the same as a yard).

7.3.07 Solve problems involving simple unit conversions <u>within the same measurement system</u> for time and length.

Calendar

Daily Spiral Review 17-3

Problem of the Day 17-3

Quick Check 17-3

Center Activities 17-3

Reteaching 17-3

Practice 17-3

Enrichment 17-3

	Lesson **17-4** Elapsed Time pp. 400–401	Lesson **17-5** Temperature pp. 402–403
Student Edition Pages		
Illinois Mathematics Performance Descriptors	7C.Stage C.2. Determine elapsed time between events.	7C.Stage C.1. Select and apply appropriate standard units and tools to measure length, area, volume, weight, time, and temperature.
Illinois Mathematics Assessment Framework Objectives	7.3.01 Solve problems involving simple elapsed time in compound units (e.g., hours, minutes, days).	7.3.02 Select and use appropriate standard units and tools to measure length (to the nearest inch or cm), time (to the nearest minute), and temperature (to the nearest degree).
Materials	Pupil's clock face or Blank clock face (Teaching Tool 34)	
Daily Spiral Review	Daily Spiral Review 17-4	Daily Spiral Review 17-5
Problem of the Day	Problem of the Day 17-4	Problem of the Day 17-5
Interactive Learning		Interactive Learning Recording Sheet 27
Quick Check	Quick Check 17-4	Quick Check 17-5
Center Activities	Center Activities 17-4	Center Activities 17-5
Reteaching	Reteaching 17-4	Reteaching 17-5
Practice	Practice 17-4	Practice 17-5
Enrichment	Enrichment 17-4	Enrichment 17-5
Digital Resources www.pearsonsuccessnet.com	Animated Glossary	Animated Glossary

Teacher Resource Masters

Lesson 17-6

Problem Solving:
Work Backward
pp. 404–405

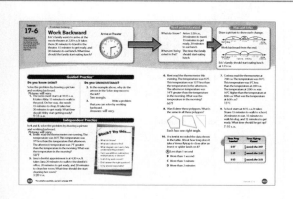

7C.Stage C.1. Select and apply appropriate standard units and tools to measure length, area, volume, weight, time, and temperature.

8.3.05 Solve word problems involving unknown quantities.

Blank clock faces (Teaching Tool 34), pupil's clock face

Daily Spiral Review 17-6

Problem of the Day 17-6

Quick Check 17-6

Center Activities 17-6

Reteaching 17-6

Practice 17-6

Enrichment 17-6

eTools

Lesson 18-1 Using Mental Math to Multiply pp. 412–413

 Lesson 18-2 Estimating Products pp. 414–415

	Lesson 18-1	**Lesson 18-2**
Illinois Mathematics Performance Descriptors	**6B.Stage C.6.** Apply knowledge of basic multiplication facts to related facts.	**6C.Stage C.2.** Select appropriate methods and tools for computing with whole numbers from mental computation, estimation, calculators, and paper/pencil according to the context and nature of the computation and use of the selected method or tool.
Illinois Mathematics Assessment Framework Objectives	**6.3.11** Model and apply basic multiplication facts, and apply them to related multiples of 10.	**6.3.14** Make estimates appropriate to a given situation with whole numbers.
	Place-value blocks, 1–9 number cards	

Teacher Resource Masters

Daily Spiral Review	Daily Spiral Review 18-1	Daily Spiral Review 18-2
Problem of the Day	Problem of the Day 18-1	Problem of the Day 18-2
Interactive Learning		
Quick Check	Quick Check 18-1	Quick Check 18-2
Center Activities	Center Activities 18-1	Center Activities 18-2
Reteaching	Reteaching 18-1	Reteaching 18-2
Practice	Practice 18-1	Practice 18-2
Enrichment	Enrichment 18-1	Enrichment 18-2
DIGITAL www.pearsonsuccessnet.com	eTools	

Topic Start-Up

- Vocabulary Cards
- Topic 18 Home-School Connection (English and Spanish)

Topic Wrap-Up

- Topic 18 Test, pages 430–431
- Topic 18 Alternate Assessments, pages 431A–431B
- Reteaching, pages 432–433

Lesson 18-3
Multiplication and Arrays
pp. 416–417

Lesson 18-4
Breaking Apart to Multiply
pp. 418–419

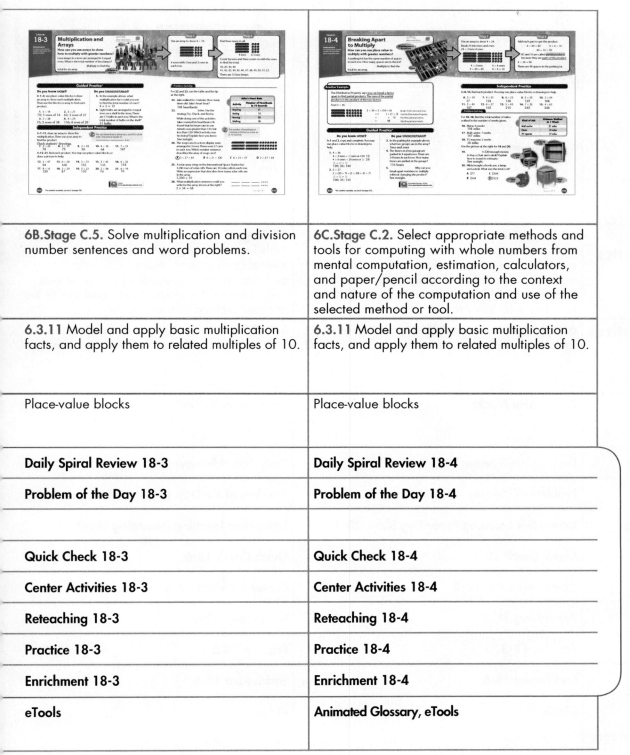

6B.Stage C.5. Solve multiplication and division number sentences and word problems.	**6C.Stage C.2.** Select appropriate methods and tools for computing with whole numbers from mental computation, estimation, calculators, and paper/pencil according to the context and nature of the computation and use of the selected method or tool.
6.3.11 Model and apply basic multiplication facts, and apply them to related multiples of 10.	**6.3.11** Model and apply basic multiplication facts, and apply them to related multiples of 10.
Place-value blocks	Place-value blocks
Daily Spiral Review 18-3	**Daily Spiral Review 18-4**
Problem of the Day 18-3	**Problem of the Day 18-4**
Quick Check 18-3	**Quick Check 18-4**
Center Activities 18-3	**Center Activities 18-4**
Reteaching 18-3	**Reteaching 18-4**
Practice 18-3	**Practice 18-4**
Enrichment 18-3	**Enrichment 18-4**
eTools	**Animated Glossary, eTools**

Lesson 18-5

Using an Expanded Algorithm
pp. 420–421

Lesson 18-6

Multiplying 2- and 3-Digit by 1-Digit Numbers
pp. 422–425

	Using an Expanded Algorithm	**Multiplying 2- and 3-Digit by 1-Digit Numbers**
Illinois Mathematics Performance Descriptors	**6C.Stage C.2.** Select appropriate methods and tools for computing with whole numbers from mental computation, estimation, calculators, and paper/pencil according to the context and nature of the computation and use of the selected method or tool.	**6C.Stage C.2.** Select appropriate methods and tools for computing with whole numbers from mental computation, estimation, calculators, and paper/pencil according to the context and nature of the computation and use of the selected method or tool.
Illinois Mathematics Assessment Framework Objectives	**6.3.11** Model and apply basic multiplication facts, and apply them to related multiples of 10.	**6.3.11** Model and apply basic multiplication facts, and apply them to related multiples of 10.
	Place-value blocks	Place-value blocks
Daily Spiral Review	**Daily Spiral Review 18-5**	**Daily Spiral Review 18-6**
Problem of the Day	**Problem of the Day 18-5**	**Problem of the Day 18-6**
Interactive Learning	**Interactive Learning Recording Sheet 28**	**Interactive Learning Recording Sheet 29**
Quick Check	**Quick Check 18-5**	**Quick Check 18-6**
Center Activities	**Center Activities 18-5**	**Center Activities 18-6**
Reteaching	**Reteaching 18-5**	**Reteaching 18-6**
Practice	**Practice 18-5**	**Practice 18-6**
Enrichment	**Enrichment 18-5**	**Enrichment 18-6**
	eTools	eTools

Teacher Resource Masters

DIGITAL www.pearsonsuccessnet.com

MATH STRAND COLORS

● Number and Operations   ● Measurement
● Algebra   ● Data Analysis and Probability
● Geometry   ● Problem Solving

Lesson 18-7

Problem Solving: Draw a Picture and Write a Number Sentence pp. 426–429

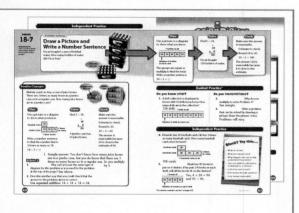

6B.Stage C.5. Solve multiplication and division number sentences and word problems.

8.3.05 Solve word problems involving unknown quantities.

Daily Spiral Review 18-7

Problem of the Day 18-7

Quick Check 18-7

Center Activities 18-7

Reteaching 18-7

Practice 18-7

Enrichment 18-7

Dividing with 1-Digit Numbers
ILLINOIS TOPIC PLANNER
Pacing: 1 lesson per day

	Lesson 19-1 Mental Math pp. 436–437	**Lesson 19-2** Estimating Quotients pp. 438–439
Illinois Mathematics Performance Descriptors	**6C.Stage C.2.** Select appropriate methods and tools for computing with whole numbers from mental computation, estimation, calculators, and paper/pencil according to the context and nature of the computation and use of the selected method or tool.	**6C.Stage C.1.** Develop and use strategies to estimate the results of whole-number computations and to judge the reasonableness of such results.
Illinois Mathematics Assessment Framework Objectives	Previews Grade 4: **6.4.12** Model and apply basic multiplication and division facts, and apply them to related multiples of 10.	**6.3.14** Make estimates appropriate to a given situation with whole numbers.
	Place-value blocks	
Daily Spiral Review	Daily Spiral Review 19-1	Daily Spiral Review 19-2
Problem of the Day	Problem of the Day 19-1	Problem of the Day 19-2
Interactive Learning		
Quick Check	Quick Check 19-1	Quick Check 19-2
Center Activities	Center Activities 19-1	Center Activities 19-2
Reteaching	Reteaching 19-1	Reteaching 19-2
Practice	Practice 19-1	Practice 19-2
Enrichment	Enrichment 19-1	Enrichment 19-2
DIGITAL www.pearsonsuccessnet.com		

Teacher Resource Masters

Topic Start-Up
- Vocabulary Cards
- Topic 19 Home-School Connection (English and Spanish)

Topic Wrap-Up
- Topic 19 Test, pages 452–453
- Topic 19 Alternate Assessments, pages 453A–453B

- Reteaching, pages 454–455

MATH STRAND COLORS

● Number and Operations
● Algebra
● Geometry
● Measurement
● Data Analysis and Probability
● Problem Solving

Lesson 19-3

Connecting Models and Symbols
pp. 440–443

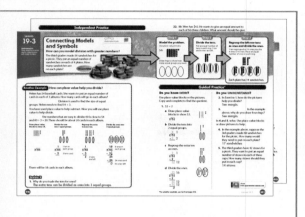

6B.Stage C.2. Demonstrate and describe the effects of multiplying and dividing whole numbers using appropriate mathematical notation and vocabulary.

6.3.01 Read, write, recognize, and model equivalent representations of whole numbers and their place values up to 100,000.

Place-value blocks

Daily Spiral Review 19-3

Problem of the Day 19-3

Quick Check 19-3

Center Activities 19-3

Reteaching 19-3

Practice 19-3

Enrichment 19-3

eTools

		Lesson 19-4 Dividing 2-Digit Numbers pp. 444–445	**Lesson 19-5** Dividing with Remainders pp. 446–447
	Illinois Mathematics Performance Descriptors	6C.Stage C.2. Select appropriate methods and tools for computing with whole numbers from mental computation, estimation, calculators, and paper/pencil according to the context and nature of the computation and use of the selected method or tool.	6C.Stage C.2. Select appropriate methods and tools for computing with whole numbers from mental computation, estimation, calculators, and paper/pencil according to the context and nature of the computation and use of the selected method or tool.
	Illinois Mathematics Assessment Framework Objectives	Previews Grade 5: 6.5.12 Solve problems and number sentences involving addition, subtraction, multiplication, and division using whole numbers.	Previews Grade 5: 6.5.12 Solve problems and number sentences involving addition, subtraction, multiplication, and division using whole numbers.
		Place-value blocks	Two-color counters
	Daily Spiral Review	Daily Spiral Review 19-4	Daily Spiral Review 19-5
	Problem of the Day	Problem of the Day 19-4	Problem of the Day 19-5
	Interactive Learning		
	Quick Check	Quick Check 19-4	Quick Check 19-5
	Center Activities	Center Activities 19-4	Center Activities 19-5
	Reteaching	Reteaching 19-4	Reteaching 19-5
	Practice	Practice 19-4	Practice 19-5
	Enrichment	Enrichment 19-4	Enrichment 19-5
			Animated Glossary, eTools

Teacher Resource Masters

www.pearsonsuccessnet.com

Lesson 19-6

Problem Solving:
Multiple-Step Problems
pp. 448–451

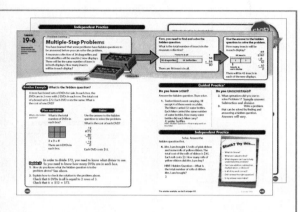

6B.Stage C.5. Solve multiplication and division number sentences and word problems.

8.3.05 Solve word problems involving unknown quantities.

Daily Spiral Review 19-6

Problem of the Day 19-6

Quick Check 19-6

Center Activities 19-6

Reteaching 19-6

Practice 19-6

Enrichment 19-6

	Lesson 20-1 Organizing Data pp. 458–459	**Lesson 20-2** Reading Pictographs and Bar Graphs pp. 460–463
Student Edition Pages	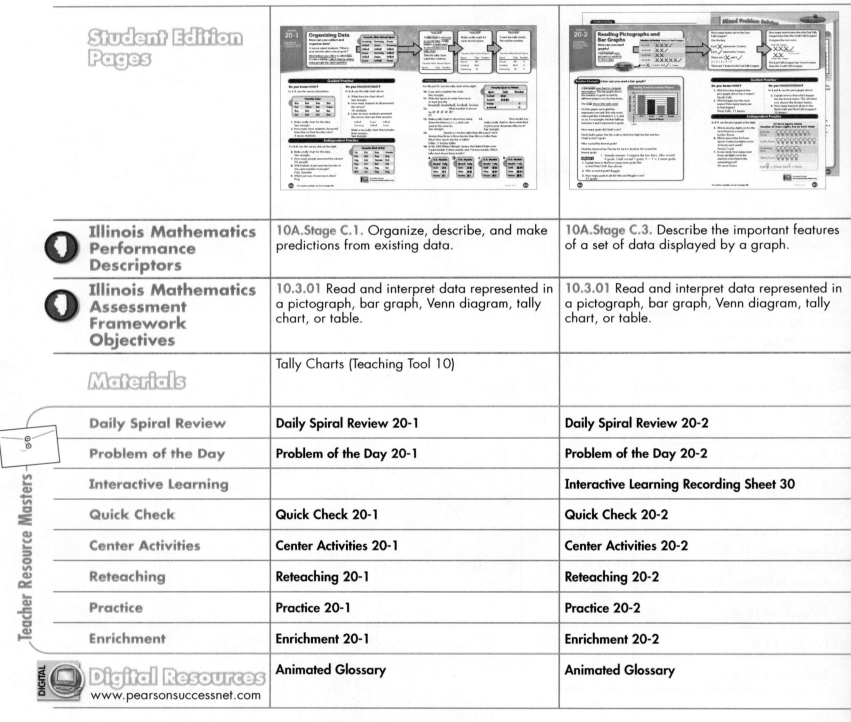	
Illinois Mathematics Performance Descriptors	10A.Stage C.1. Organize, describe, and make predictions from existing data.	10A.Stage C.3. Describe the important features of a set of data displayed by a graph.
Illinois Mathematics Assessment Framework Objectives	10.3.01 Read and interpret data represented in a pictograph, bar graph, Venn diagram, tally chart, or table.	10.3.01 Read and interpret data represented in a pictograph, bar graph, Venn diagram, tally chart, or table.
Materials	Tally Charts (Teaching Tool 10)	
Daily Spiral Review	Daily Spiral Review 20-1	Daily Spiral Review 20-2
Problem of the Day	Problem of the Day 20-1	Problem of the Day 20-2
Interactive Learning		Interactive Learning Recording Sheet 30
Quick Check	Quick Check 20-1	Quick Check 20-2
Center Activities	Center Activities 20-1	Center Activities 20-2
Reteaching	Reteaching 20-1	Reteaching 20-2
Practice	Practice 20-1	Practice 20-2
Enrichment	Enrichment 20-1	Enrichment 20-2
Digital Resources www.pearsonsuccessnet.com	Animated Glossary	Animated Glossary

Teacher Resource Masters

Topic Start-Up

- Vocabulary Card Sets A–D
- Topic 20 Home-School Connection (English and Spanish)

Topic Wrap-Up

- Topic 20 Test, pages 484–485
- Topic 20 Alternate Assessments, pages 485A–485B

- Reteaching, pages 486–487
- Cumulative Test Topics 1–20, pages 487A–487B
- Benchmark Test Topics 17–20, pages 487C–487D

MATH STRAND COLORS

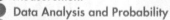

● Number and Operations   ● Measurement
● Algebra   ● Data Analysis and Probability
● Geometry   ● Problem Solving

 Lesson 20-3   **Making Pictographs** pp. 464–465

 Lesson 20-4   **Making Bar Graphs** pp. 466–467

 Lesson 20-5   **Ordered Pairs and Line Graphs** pp. 468–471

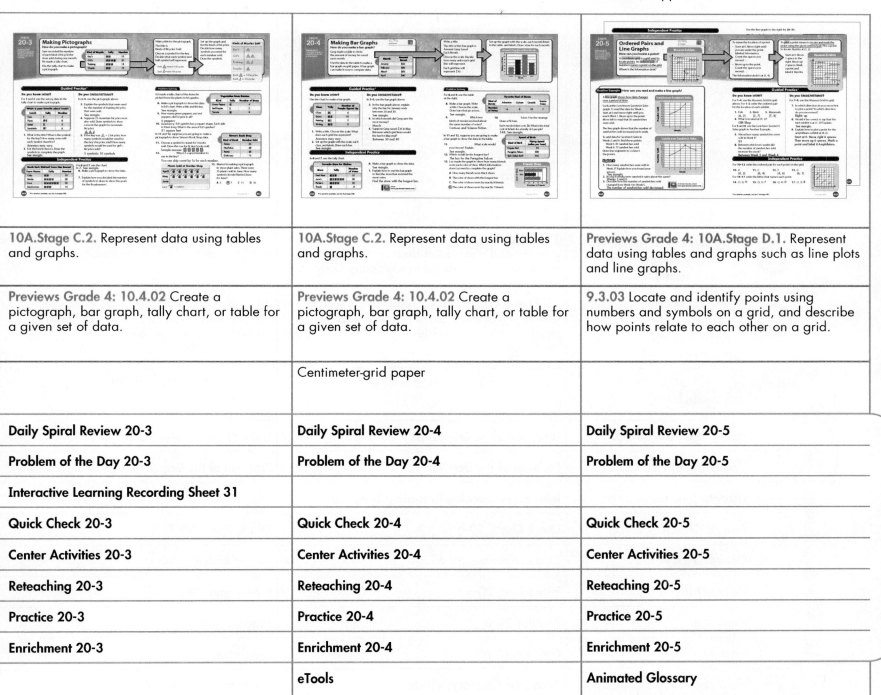

Making Pictographs	Making Bar Graphs	Ordered Pairs and Line Graphs
10A.Stage C.2. Represent data using tables and graphs.	**10A.Stage C.2.** Represent data using tables and graphs.	**Previews Grade 4: 10A.Stage D.1.** Represent data using tables and graphs such as line plots and line graphs.
Previews Grade 4: 10.4.02 Create a pictograph, bar graph, tally chart, or table for a given set of data.	Previews Grade 4: 10.4.02 Create a pictograph, bar graph, tally chart, or table for a given set of data.	9.3.03 Locate and identify points using numbers and symbols on a grid, and describe how points relate to each other on a grid.
	Centimeter-grid paper	
Daily Spiral Review 20-3	**Daily Spiral Review 20-4**	**Daily Spiral Review 20-5**
Problem of the Day 20-3	**Problem of the Day 20-4**	**Problem of the Day 20-5**
Interactive Learning Recording Sheet 31		
Quick Check 20-3	**Quick Check 20-4**	**Quick Check 20-5**
Center Activities 20-3	**Center Activities 20-4**	**Center Activities 20-5**
Reteaching 20-3	**Reteaching 20-4**	**Reteaching 20-5**
Practice 20-3	**Practice 20-4**	**Practice 20-5**
Enrichment 20-3	**Enrichment 20-4**	**Enrichment 20-5**
	eTools	**Animated Glossary**

Lesson 20-6 How Likely? pp. 472–475	Lesson 20-7 Outcomes and Experiments pp. 476–477

Student Edition Pages		
Illinois Mathematics Performance Descriptors	**10C.Stage C.1.** Describe events as likely or unlikely and discuss the degree of likelihood using such words as certain, equally likely, and impossible.	**10C.Stage C.3.** Make predictions based on the results received from a probability experiment.
Illinois Mathematics Assessment Framework Objectives	**10.3.04** Classify events using words such as certain, most likely, equally likely, least likely, possible, and impossible.	**10.3.04** Classify events using words such as certain, most likely, equally likely, least likely, possible, and impossible.
Materials		Spinners (Teaching Tool 23), crayons
Daily Spiral Review	**Daily Spiral Review 20-6**	**Daily Spiral Review 20-7**
Problem of the Day	**Problem of the Day 20-6**	**Problem of the Day 20-7**
Interactive Learning	**Interactive Learning Recording Sheet 32**	
Quick Check	**Quick Check 20-6**	**Quick Check 20-7**
Center Activities	**Center Activities 20-6**	**Center Activities 20-7**
Reteaching	**Reteaching 20-6**	**Reteaching 20-7**
Practice	**Practice 20-6**	**Practice 20-7**
Enrichment	**Enrichment 20-6**	**Enrichment 20-7**
Digital Resources www.pearsonsuccessnet.com	**Animated Glossary, eTools**	**Animated Glossary, eTools**

Teacher Resource Masters

Lesson 20-8 Line Plots and Probability pp. 478–481

 Lesson 20-9 Problem Solving: Use Tables and Graphs to Draw Conclusions pp. 482–483

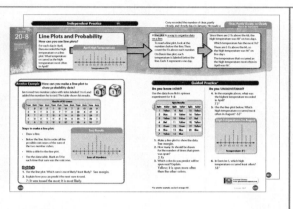

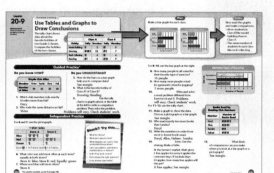

Previews Grade 4: 10A.Stage D.1. Represent data using tables and graphs.	10A.Stage C.1. Organize, describe, and make predictions from existing data.
Previews Grade 4: 10.4.01 Read and interpret data represented in a pictograph, bar graph, line plot, Venn diagram, tally chart, table, line graph, or circle graph.	10.3.01 Read and interpret data represented in a pictograph, bar graph, Venn diagram, tally chart, or table.
	Sandwich survey (Teaching Tool 44)
Daily Spiral Review 20-8	Daily Spiral Review 20-9
Problem of the Day 20-8	Problem of the Day 20-9
Interactive Learning Recording Sheet 33	
Quick Check 20-8	Quick Check 20-9
Center Activities 20-8	Center Activities 20-9
Reteaching 20-8	Reteaching 20-9
Practice 20-8	Practice 20-9
Enrichment 20-8	Enrichment 20-9
Animated Glossary	

SCOPE AND SEQUENCE

For each row in the scope and sequence chart, sample page references are given. For complete references, see the index in this book, beginning on page T175.

NUMBER AND OPERATIONS

	Pre-K	K	1	2	3	4	5	6	Grade 3 Pages
Whole Number Concepts									
One–to–one correspondence									
Relating sets of objects to numerals									
Using ordinal numbers for position									10–11
Counting, reading, writing, renaming									
Numbers to 10									10–11
Numbers to 100									4–5
Numbers to 1,000									4–5
Numbers to 1,000,000									6–7, 8–9, 10–11
Numbers in millions									
Billions and trillions									
Concrete/pictorial and number-line models									4–5, 6–7, 8–9, 12–14, 16–17, 40–42
Comparing and ordering									12–14, 16–17
Forms of numbers (standard form, expanded form)									4–5, 6–7, 8–9
Place value									4–5, 6–7, 8–9, 10–11, 12–14, 18–20
Place-value relationships and patterns									4–5, 6–7, 8–9, 12–14, 15, 16–17, 24–25
Skip counting									18–21, 34–35, 68–70, 208–209
Rounding									40–42, 44–46, 74–76
Money									
Counting and showing amounts									
Penny, nickel, dime									18–21, 308–311
Quarter, half dollar, dollar									18–21, 308–311
Value of collection of coins									18–21, 308–311
Comparing amounts									18–21, 308–311
Making change									22–23, 312–314
Using dollar sign and decimal point									18–21, 308–311
Rounding to nearest dollar									18–21, 308–311
Fraction Concepts									
Showing concrete/pictorial models for part of a whole									276–277, 278–279, 282–283
Describing part of a whole or set									276–277, 278–279, 280–281, 282–283
Reading and writing fractions									278–279, 280–281
Rounding/estimating									282–283
Comparing and ordering using models									288–289
Comparing using common denominators									288–289
Models for equivalent fractions									284–286
Lowest terms/simplest form									
Mixed numbers, fractions greater than 1									
Fractions on a number line									290–293
Related to decimals									306–307
Rational numbers									

☐ Early Experience ▨ Introduce ■ Develop ▨ Master and Apply

	Pre-K	K	1	2	3	4	5	6	Grade 3 Pages
Decimal Concepts									
Meaning									306–307
Decimal notation for money									18–21, 308–311
Concrete/pictorial models									308–311
Tenths and hundredths									308–311
Thousandths									
Equivalent decimals and place value									
Fractions as decimals									
Related to measurement (metric system)									
Decimals on a number line									
Comparing and ordering									
Rounding									
Scientific notation									
Integer Concepts and Operations									
Meaning									
Comparing and ordering									
Adding and subtracting									
Multiplying and dividing									
Ordered pairs with integers									
Equations with integers									
Integer patterns									
Estimation and Mental Math Strategies									
Deciding when to estimate									44–46, 74–76
Rounding to nearest 10									40–42, 44–46, 74–76
Rounding to nearest 100									40–42, 44–46, 74–76
Rounding to nearest 1,000									
Substituting compatible numbers									44–46, 74–76
Determining reasonableness of results									78–79
Counting on or back									18–21, 34–35, 68–70
Using 10s or 100s to add or subtract									34–35, 36–38, 44–45, 54–55, 68–70, 72–73
Breaking apart numbers									36–38, 52–141, 142–143, 144–146, 148–149
Using patterns to multiply by 10 or 100									412–413, 414–415
Using multiplication and division patterns									108–109, 110–112, 170–171, 184–185
Using the distributive property									

□ Early Experience　■ Introduce　■ Develop　■ Master and Apply

NUMBER AND OPERATIONS

	Pre-K	K	1	2	3	4	5	6	Grade 3 Pages
Whole-Number Addition									
Addition stories/meanings									32–33
Related to subtraction									66–67
Basic facts and fact strategies									32–33
Fact families									66–67
Properties									32–33
Using concrete/pictorial models									32–33, 34–35, 48–49, 50–52, 54–55, 56–57
Addition number sentences									32–33, 58–59
Adding on a 100 chart									34–35
Adding 2-digit numbers									34–35, 36–38, 48–49
Adding 3-digit numbers									50–52, 54–55
Adding numbers with 4 or more digits									
Adding money									58–59, 132–133, 312–314
Three or more addends									56–57
Choosing whether to add or subtract									98–100
Addition expressions and equations									71, 216–217
Estimation and mental math									34–35, 36–38, 44–46
Problem solving									32–33, 34–35, 36–38, 44–47, 48–49, 50–52
Whole-Number Subtraction									
Subtraction stories/meanings									66–67
Related to addition									66–67
Basic facts and fact strategies									66–67
Properties									66–67
Using concrete/pictorial models									66–67, 68–70, 86–87, 88–89, 90–91, 92–94
Subtraction number sentences									66–67, 71
Subtracting on 100 chart									68–70
Subtracting 2-digit numbers									68–70, 72–73, 86–87, 88–89
Subtracting 3-digit numbers									74–76, 90–91, 92–94, 96–97
Subtracting 4-digit numbers									74–76, 90–97
Subtracting money									69, 72–73, 90, 312–314
Choosing whether to add or subtract									98–100
Subtraction expressions and equations									71, 216–217
Inverse operations									66
Estimation and mental math									68–70, 72–73, 74–76
Problem solving									66–67, 68–70, 72–73, 74–77, 78–79, 86–87

☐ Early Experience   ▨ Introduce   ■ Develop   ▩ Master and Apply

NUMBER AND OPERATIONS

	Pre-K	K	1	2	3	4	5	6	Grade 3 Pages
Whole-Number Multiplication									
Multiplication stories/meanings									108–109, 110–112, 114–115, 116–117
Related to joining equal groups									108–109
Related to addition or skip counting									108–109
Related to arrays or area models									110–112
Related to comparison ("times as many")									114–115
Basic facts and fact strategies									122–124, 126–127, 128–129, 130–131
Fact families									190–191, 192–193, 206–208
Multiplication table (fact table)									190–191
Three factors									152–153
Properties									110, 131, 153
Using concrete/pictorial models									108–109, 110–112, 114–115
Multiplication number sentences									108–109
By a 1-digit number									418–419, 420–421, 422–424
By a 2-digit number									
Multiplying money									114–115, 132–133
By multiples of 10 and 100									126–127, 156–157, 412–413
Partial products									418–419, 420–421
By a multi-digit number									
Multiplication expressions and equations									147, 216–217
Missing factors									117, 124, 184, 421, 425
Common factors									
Greatest common factor (GCF)									
Least common multiple (LCM)									
Prime and composite numbers									
Estimation and mental math									412–413, 414–415
Problem solving									108–109, 110–112, 114–115, 116–117

☐ Early Experience　▨ Introduce　■ Develop　▨ Master and Apply

NUMBER AND OPERATIONS

	Pre-K	K	1	2	3	4	5	6	Grade 3 Pages
Whole-Number Division									
Division stories/meanings	▢			I	D	D	M		164–165, 170–171, 172–173, 184–185
Related to subtraction					D		M		170–171
Related to making equal groups				I	D	D			164–165
Basic facts					I	D	M		164–165, 170–171, 172–173, 184–185
Fact families					D	D	M		184–185, 190–191, 192–193, 194–195, 206–208
1 and 0 in division						D			194–195
Using concrete/pictorial models				I	D	D			164–165, 170–171, 440–443
Division number sentences				I	D				164–165
2-digit dividends					D	D			164–165, 170–171, 172–173, 184–185
By a 1-digit divisor					D	D	M		436–437, 438–439, 440–443, 444–445
Dividing money					D	D	M		436–437, 438–439, 440–443, 444–445
By multiples of 10 and 100						D	D		
By a 2-digit divisor							D	D	
3-digit dividends						D	D	D	
Interpreting remainders					D	D			166–168, 446–447
Division expressions and equations						D	D	M	209, 216–217
Factors and divisibility						I	D		
Estimation and mental math						D	D		185, 436–437, 438–439
Problem solving					D	D	D	M	164–165, 170–171, 172–173, 190–191
Fraction Operations									
Adding and subtracting with concrete/pictorial models						D	D		294–295, 296–297, 316–318
Adding and subtracting, like denominators						D	D		294–295, 296–297, 316–318
Adding and subtracting, unlike denominators							D	M	
Adding and subtracting mixed numbers							D	D	
Finding a fraction of a whole number							D		
Multiplying and dividing with concrete/pictorial models							D		
Multiplying and dividing fractions							D	D	
Multiplying and dividing mixed numbers							D	D	
Least common denominators							D	D	
Expressions/sentences/equations							D	M	
Estimation and mental math							D	D	
Problem solving						D	D	D	294–295, 296–297, 316–317

Legend: ▢ Early Experience · I Introduce · D Develop · M Master and Apply

NUMBER AND OPERATIONS

	Pre-K	K	1	2	3	4	5	6	Grade 3 Pages
Decimal Operations									
Adding and subtracting money									312–314
Multiplying and dividing money									
Adding and subtracting with concrete/pictorial models									
Adding and subtracting decimals									312–314
Multiplying and dividing with concrete/pictorial models									
Multiplying and dividing decimals									
Multiplying and dividing by 10, 100, and 1,000									
Scientific notation									
Expressions/sentences/equations									
Estimation and mental math									
Problem solving									312–314
Ratios, Proportions, and Percents									
Meaning of ratio									
Meaning of percent									
Relating fractions, decimals, percents									
Finding percent of a number									
Finding percents less than 1 or greater than 100									
Rates and unit rates									
Proportions									
Similar figures and scale drawings									
Distance, rate, and time									
Estimating percent									
Tips, taxes, discounts, and interest									

☐ Early Experience   ▨ Introduce   ■ Develop   ▦ Master and Apply

ALGEBRA

	Pre-K	K	1	2	3	4	5	6	Grade 3 Pages
Patterns and Relationships									
Sorting and classifying objects									
Patterns with objects/geometric figures									206–207, 218–221
Skip counting									15, 208–209
Repeating patterns									206–207
Patterns in place value									6–7, 8–9, 412–413
Number patterns/sequences									208–209
Describing patterns in lists, tables, charts, and diagrams									210–211, 212–214
Making generalizations and predictions									210–211, 212–214, 252–253
Writing/evaluating numerical expressions									71, 147, 209, 216–217, 222–223
Writing/evaluating expressions with parentheses									425
Evaluating expressions with variables by substitution									222–223
Writing number pairs for a situation									210–211, 212–214
Extending patterns in tables									210–211, 212–214
Writing equations for number pair patterns									
Addition properties									33, 95
Multiplication properties									110, 131, 153
Distributive property									
Patterns in related addition and subtraction sentences									66–67
Patterns in related multiplication and division sentences									184–185, 190–191, 192–193, 206–208, 214–216
Ordered pairs									468–471
Functions									210–211
Prime and composite numbers									
Number Sentences, Equations, and Inequalities									
Modeling problem situations with objects									32–33, 66–67, 110–112, 114–115, 164–165
Completing number sentences									32–33, 66–67, 71, 95, 108–109, 164–165, 209
Writing number stories for number sentences									116–117, 172–173
Finding missing addends, subtrahends, minuends									66, 71, 95
Finding missing factors									184, 425
Equations that use letters as variables									
Expressing relationships using equations									43, 95, 209, 222–223
Expressing relationships using inequalities									222–223
Solving inequalities									
Solving equations using tables, graphs, and models									222
Solving one-step equations									
Solving two-step equations									
Graphing linear equations or functions									
Solving problems using formulas									

 Early Experience   Introduce 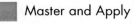 Develop Master and Apply

SCOPE AND SEQUENCE

MEASUREMENT

	Pre-K	K	1	2	3	4	5	6	Grade 3 Pages
Time and Temperature									
Sequencing events									
Compare and order by duration									
Calendar									398–399
Nearest hour/half hour									392–394
Minutes before/after the hour									396–397
Elapsed time									400–401, 404–405
Estimating time									400–401, 404–405
Equivalent times									392–394, 398–399
Changing or converting units									398–399
Comparing situations by temperature									402–403
Reading a thermometer									402–403
Temperature change									
Length and Perimeter									
Compare attributes of objects									
Comparing and ordering using direct comparison									328–331
Measuring with non-standard units									328–331
Relate size of units to number of units									328–331
Estimating and measuring with customary units									328–331, 332–333, 334–337
Estimating and measuring with metric units									350–351, 352–354
Changing or converting units									334–337, 352–354, 355
Measuring perimeter									368–369, 370–371, 372–373
Perimeter formulas									
Circumference									
Relating customary and metric measures									
Precision									

☐ Early Experience   ▨ Introduce   ▨ Develop   ▨ Master and Apply

MEASUREMENT

	Pre-K	K	1	2	3	4	5	6	Grade 3 Pages
Area									
Measuring with square units				Introduce	Develop	Develop	Develop	Master and Apply	376–377, 378–379
Estimating and measuring with customary units					Introduce	Develop	Develop	Master and Apply	376–377, 378–379
Estimating and measuring with metric units					Introduce	Develop	Develop	Master and Apply	376–377, 378–379
Area of squares and other rectangles				Introduce	Develop	Develop	Develop	Master and Apply	194–196, 376–377
Area of parallelograms and triangles							Introduce	Develop	
Area of irregular shapes							Introduce	Develop	
Area formulas							Introduce	Develop	
Area of circles								Master and Apply	
Surface area							Introduce	Develop	
Length/perimeter/area relationships						Develop	Develop	Master and Apply	372–373
Weight/Mass									
Comparing and ordering using direct comparison	Early Experience	Introduce	Develop	Develop	Develop	Develop	Master and Apply		340–341, 358–359
Measuring with non-standard units	Early Experience	Introduce	Develop	Develop	Develop	Develop	Master and Apply		340–341, 358–359
Estimating and measuring with customary units				Introduce	Develop	Develop	Develop	Master and Apply	340–341
Estimating and measuring with metric units				Introduce	Develop	Develop	Develop	Master and Apply	358–359
Changing or converting units					Develop	Develop	Develop	Master and Apply	340–341, 358–359
Capacity/Volume									
Comparing and ordering using direct comparison	Early Experience	Introduce	Develop	Develop	Develop	Develop	Master and Apply		338–339, 356–357
Measuring capacity with non-standard units	Early Experience	Introduce	Introduce	Develop	Develop	Develop	Master and Apply		338–339
Estimating and measuring volume with cubic units				Introduce	Develop	Develop	Develop	Master and Apply	380–382
Estimating and measuring capacity with customary units			Introduce	Introduce	Develop	Develop	Develop	Master and Apply	338–339
Estimating and measuring capacity with metric units			Introduce	Introduce	Develop	Develop	Develop	Master and Apply	356–357
Changing or converting units					Develop	Develop	Develop	Master and Apply	338–339, 356–357
Volume of a rectangular prism formula					Introduce	Develop	Develop	Master and Apply	380–382
Volume of a triangular prisms and cylinders							Introduce	Develop	
Volume of irregular solids							Introduce	Develop	

☐ Early Experience   ▨ Introduce   ■ Develop   ▨ Master and Apply

SCOPE AND SEQUENCE

GEOMETRY

	Pre-K	K	1	2	3	4	5	6	Grade 3 Pages
Plane and Solid Figures									
Spatial reasoning: over, under, above, below									
Sorting shapes by attributes									
Geometric models for real-world situations									234–237, 238–313, 242–243, 244–245
Circles, rectangles, squares, triangles									238–240, 248–249, 250–251
Other polygons									246–247
Spheres, rectangular solids, cylinders, cones									234–237
Other solids									
Describing shapes									238–240, 242–243, 244–245, 246–247
Drawing figures from descriptions									252–253, 266–267
Relating plane and solid figures									238–239
Views of solid figures									342–343
Combining shapes									268–269
Subdividing shapes									264–265
Faces, edges, vertices									238–240
Classifying polygons									246–247, 252–253
Classifying triangles									248–249
Classifying quadrilaterals									250–251
Making conjectures about geometric relationships									
Angles									
Right, obtuse, acute angles									244–245
Parallel and perpendicular									
Measuring and drawing angles									
Angles in polygons									
Angle pairs									
Symmetry, Congruence, and Transformations									
Symmetry									264–265, 266–267, 268–269
Congruent figures									260–262
Transformations (reflections, translations, rotations)									260–262
Number Lines and the Coordinate Plane									
Points named by whole numbers									468–471
Points named by fractions/decimals									
Using coordinate grids									468–471
Ordered pairs									468–471
Segment lengths on the coordinate plane									

☐ Early Experience ▨ Introduce ■ Develop ▥ Master and Apply

DATA ANALYSIS AND PROBABILITY

	Pre-K	K	1	2	3	4	5	6	Grade 3 Pages
Reading and Making Graphs									
Pictographs/real graphs									460–462, 464–465
Bar graphs									460–462, 466–467, 482–483
Line graphs									
Circle graphs									
Histograms									
Line plots									478–481
Stem-and-leaf plots									
Making predictions from graphs									478–481
Choosing appropriate graphs									460–462, 464–465, 466–467
Data Collection and Analysis									
Sorting objects									
Tally charts									458–459, 464–465, 472–475, 482–483
Reading charts/tables									458–459, 464–465, 466–467, 472–475, 482–483
Collecting and organizing data									458–459, 464–465, 466–467
Describing sets of data									460–462, 472–475, 482–483
Comparing related sets of data									482–483
Making charts/tables									458–459
Frequency tables									
Surveys									458–459, 464–465, 466–467, 482–483
Interpreting data and making predictions									460–462, 472–475, 478–481, 482–483
Range and mode									
Mean									
Median									
Probability									
Likely/unlikely events									472–475
More/less/equally likely									472–475
Certain/possible/impossible events									
Using fractions to describe results									472–475
Experiments									472–475, 476–477
Outcomes									472–475, 476–477, 478–481
Tree diagrams									
Making predictions									472–475, 476–477, 478–481
Combinations									
Permutations									
Independent and dependent events									

☐ Early Experience   ▨ Introduce   ▧ Develop   ▩ Master and Apply

PROBLEM SOLVING

	Pre-K	K	1	2	3	4	5	6	Grade 3 Pages
Problem-Solving Skills and Strategies									
Use data from a picture, graph, or table									482–483
Extra or missing information									320–321
Two-question problems									132–133
Multiple-step problems									154–156
Draw a picture									58–59, 98–99, 196–197, 207, 426–428
Make an organized list									24–25
Make a table or graph									298–299, 360–361
Act it out, use objects									194–196, 224–226, 342–343
Look for a pattern									298–299, 360–361
Try, check, and revise									374–375
Write a number sentence or equation									196–197
Work backward									404–405
Solve a simpler problem									384–385
Evaluate solutions for reasonableness									78–79
Make and test generalizations and conjectures									252–253
Reasoning, Communication, Connections									
Comparing/contrasting									12–14, 206–207, 208–209, 210–211, 212–214
Classifying/sorting									234–237, 238–240, 242–243, 244–245
Finding/extending/using patterns									298–299, 360–361
Making and testing generalizations from examples and non-examples									252–253
Drawing conclusions and evaluating arguments									118–120, 132
Evaluate solutions for reasonableness									12–14, 17, 40–42, 44–46, 48–49, 54–55, 56–57
Communicating ideas with objects, words, pictures, and numbers									20, 33, 58–59, 98–99, 141, 194–196, 196–197
Explaining a solution process									3, 5, 7, 8, 13, 14, 16, 17, 24, 27, 32, 38, 41, 42
Recording observations using objects, words, pictures, and numbers									58, 98–100, 118–120, 194–196, 196–198
Relating informal language to math language and symbols									32–33, 43, 66–67, 71, 108–109, 114–115
Making connections between mathematics strands									5, 7, 9, 13, 14, 17, 19, 20, 21, 25, 33, 35, 37
Making connections to other curriculum areas									47, 77, 113, 169, 215, 313, 463
Making connections to daily life									4–5, 6–7, 8–9, 12–14, 16–17, 18–21, 32–33
Representation									
Whole-number addition/subtraction using concrete/pictorial models									32–33, 34–35, 48–49, 50–52, 54–55, 56–57
Whole-number multiplication/division using concrete/pictorial models									108–109, 110–112, 114–115, 164–165, 170–171
Concrete/pictorial models for part of a whole/set									244–245, 276–277, 278–279, 280–281
Fractions on a number line									
Fraction operations using pictorial models									294–295, 296–297, 316–318
Pictorial models for decimals									308–311
Decimals on a number line									
Decimal operations using pictorial models									
Similar figures and scale drawings									
Counting units to find length, area, volume									328–331, 376–377, 378–379, 380–382
Geometric models for real-world situations									234–237, 238–240, 242–243, 244–245
Solving problems by drawing a picture/diagram									58–59, 98–100, 196–198, 426–428
Making graphs/charts/tables/diagrams									298–299, 360–361, 458–459, 464–465, 472–475
Number sentences and equations to model real situations									32–33, 43, 58–59, 66–67, 71, 95, 108–109

☐ Early Experience   ▨ Introduce   ▨ Develop   ▨ Master and Apply

Glossary

A

A.M. Time between midnight and noon.

acute angle An angle that measures less than a right angle.

acute triangle A triangle with three acute angles.

addends Numbers added together to give a sum.
Example: 2 + 7 = 9
Addend   Addend

angle A figure formed by two rays that have the same endpoint.

area The number of square units needed to cover a region.

array A way of displaying objects in rows and columns.

Associative (Grouping) Property of Addition The grouping of addends can be changed and the sum will be the same.

Associative (Grouping) Property of Multiplication The grouping of factors can be changed and the product will be the same.

B

bar graph A graph using bars to show data.

benchmark fraction A commonly used fraction such as $\frac{1}{4}, \frac{1}{3}, \frac{1}{2}, \frac{2}{3}$, and $\frac{3}{4}$.

C

capacity The volume of a container measured in liquid units.

centimeter (cm) A metric unit of length.

certain event An event that is sure to happen.

Commutative (Order) Property of Addition Numbers can be added in any order and the sum will be the same.

Commutative (Order) Property of Multiplication Numbers can be multiplied in any order and the product will be the same.

compare To decide if one number is greater than or less than another number.

compatible numbers Numbers that are easy to add, subtract, multiply or divide mentally.

cone A solid figure with a circle as its base and a curved surface that meets at a point.

congruent figures Figures that have the same shape and size.

coordinate grid A grid used to show ordered pairs.

corner The point where 3 or more edges meet in a solid figure.

cube A solid figure with six faces that are congruent squares.

cubic unit A cube with edges 1 unit long, used to measure volume.

cup A customary unit of capacity.

cylinder A solid figure with two congruent circles as bases.

D

data Pieces of information.

decimal A number with one or more digits to the right of the decimal point.

decimal point A dot used to separate dollars from cents in money and ones from tenths in a number.

decimeter (dm) A metric unit of length. 1 decimeter equals 10 centimeters.

degree Celsius (°C) A metric unit of temperature.

degree Fahrenheit (°F) A customary unit of temperature.

GLOSSARY

Student Edition Glossary

Vocabulary Cards are provided in the Teacher Resource Masters.

Animated Glossary is provided in the Digital Student Edition.

denominator The number below the fraction bar in a fraction, the total number of equal parts in all.

difference The answer when subtracting two numbers.

digits The symbols 0, 1, 2, 3, 4, 5, 6, 7, 8, and 9 used to write numbers.

Distributive Property One factor in a multiplication problem can be broken apart to find partial products. The sum of the partial products is the product of the two factors.
Example: $(4 \times 28) = (4 \times 20) + (4 \times 8)$

dividend The number to be divided.
Example: $63 \div 9 = 7$
Dividend

divisible Can be divided by another number without leaving a remainder.
Example: 10 is divisible by 2.

division An operation that tells how many equal groups there are or how many are in each group.

divisor The number by which another number is divided.
Example: $63 \div 9 = 7$
Divisor

dollar sign ($) A symbol used to indicate money.

E

edge A line segment where two faces of a solid figure meet.

eighth One of 8 equal parts of a whole.

elapsed time Total amount of time that passes from the beginning time to the ending time.

equally likely outcomes Outcomes that have the same chance of happening.

equation A number sentence that uses = (is equal to).

equilateral triangle A triangle with all sides the same length.

equivalent fractions Fractions that name the same part of a whole, same part of a set, or same location on a number line.

estimate To give an approximate number or answer.

even number A whole number that has 0, 2, 4, 6, or 8 in the ones place; A number that is a multiple of 2.

expanded form A number written as the sum of the values of its digits.
Example: $2,476 = 2,000 + 400 + 70 + 6$

F

face A flat surface of a solid that does not roll.

fact family A group of related facts using the same numbers.

factors Numbers that are multiplied together to give a product.
Example: $7 \times 3 = 21$
Factor   Factor

fifth One of 5 equal parts of a whole.

flip (reflection) The change in the position that picks up and moves a figure to give a mirror image.
Example:

Figure A is flipped to make figure B.

foot (ft) A customary unit of length. 1 foot equals 12 inches.

fourth One of 4 equal parts of a whole.

fraction A symbol, such as $\frac{2}{8}, \frac{5}{1},$ or $\frac{5}{5}$, used to name a part of a whole, a part of a set, or a location on a number line.

G

gallon (gal) A customary unit of capacity. 1 gallon equals 4 quarts.

gram (g) A metric unit of mass, the amount of matter in an object.

H

half (plural, halves) One of 2 equal parts of a whole.

half hour A unit of time equal to 30 minutes.

hexagon A polygon with 6 sides.

hour A unit of time equal to 60 minutes.

hundredth One of 100 equal parts of a whole, written as 0.01 or $\frac{1}{100}$.

Identity (One) Property of Multiplication The product of any number and 1 is that number.

Identity (Zero) Property of Addition The sum of any number and zero is that same number.

impossible event An event that will never happen.

inch (in.) A customary unit of length.

inequality A number sentence that uses < (is less than) or > (is greater than).

intersecting lines Lines that cross at one point.

isosceles triangle A triangle with at least two sides the same length.

key Explanation of what each symbol represents in a pictograph.

kilogram (kg) A metric unit of mass, the amount of matter in an object. 1 kilogram equals 1,000 grams.

kilometer (km) A metric unit of length. 1 kilometer equals 1,000 meters.

likely event An event that will probably happen.

line A straight path of points that is endless in both directions.

line graph A graph that shows how data changes over a period of time.

line of symmetry A line on which a figure can be folded so that both parts match exactly.

Line of symmetry

line plot A way to organize data on a line.

line segment A part of a line that has two endpoints.

liter (L) A metric unit of capacity. 1 liter equals 1,000 milliliters.

meter (m) A metric unit of length. 1 meter equals 100 centimeters.

mile (mi) A customary unit of length. 1 mile equals 5,280 feet.

milliliter (mL) A metric unit of capacity. 1,000 milliliters equals 1 liter.

millimeter (mm) A metric unit of length. 1,000 millimeters equals 1 meter.

minute A unit of time equal to 60 seconds.

mixed number A number with a whole number part and a fraction part.
Example: $2\frac{3}{4}$

multiple The product of the number and any other whole number.
Example: 0, 4, 8, 12, and 16 are multiples of 4.

multiplication An operation that gives the total number when you put together equal groups.

number line A line that shows numbers in order using a scale.
Example:

numerator The number above the fraction bar in a fraction.

numerical expression An expression that contains numbers and at least one operation. A numerical expression is also called a number expression.

obtuse angle An angle that measures more than a right angle.

obtuse triangle A triangle with one obtuse angle.

octagon A polygon with 8 sides.

odd number A whole number that has 1, 3, 5, 7, or 9 in the ones place; A number not divisible by 2.

order To arrange numbers from least to greatest or from greatest to least.

ordered pair Two numbers used to name a point on a coordinate grid.

ordinal numbers Numbers used to tell the order of people or objects.

ounce (oz) A customary unit of weight.

outcome A possible result of a game or experiment.

P.M. Time between noon and midnight.

parallel lines Lines that never intersect.

parallelogram A quadrilateral in which opposite sides are parallel.

pentagon A polygon with 5 sides.

perimeter The distance around a figure.

period A group of three digits in a number, separated by a comma.

perpendicular lines Two lines that intersect to form right angles.

pictograph A graph using pictures or symbols to show data.

pint (pt) A customary unit of capacity. 1 pint equals 2 cups.

place value The value given to the place a digit has in a number. *Example:* In 3,946, the place value of the digit 9 is *hundreds*.

plot Locate and mark a point on a coordinate grid using a given ordered pair.

point An exact position often marked by a dot.

polygon A closed figure made up of straight line segments.

possible event An event that might or might not happen.

pound (lb) A customary unit of weight. 1 pound equals 16 ounces.

probability The chance an event will happen.

product The answer to a multiplication problem.

pyramid A solid figure whose base is a polygon and whose faces are triangles with a common point.

quadrilateral A polygon with 4 sides.

quart (qt) A customary unit of capacity. 1 quart equals 2 pints.

quarter hour A unit of time equal to 15 minutes

quotient The answer to a division problem.

R

ray A part of a line that has one endpoint and continues endlessly in one direction.

rectangle A quadrilateral with four right angles.

rectangular prism A solid figure with faces that are rectangles.

regroup To name a whole number in a different way. *Example:* 28 = 1 ten 18 ones.

remainder The number that is left over after dividing. *Example:* 31 ÷ 7 = 4R3
Remainder

rhombus A quadrilateral with opposite sides parallel and all sides the same length.

right angle An angle that forms a square corner.

right triangle A triangle with one right angle.

round To replace a number with a number that tells about how much or how many to the nearest ten, hundred, thousand, and so on. *Example:* 42 rounded to the nearest 10 is 40.

scale The numbers that show the units used on a graph.

scalene triangle A triangle with no sides the same length.

second A unit of time. 60 seconds equal 1 minute.

side A line segment forming part of a polygon.

simplest form A fraction with a numerator and denominator that cannot be divided by the same divisor, except 1.

sixth One of 6 equal parts of a whole.

slide (translation) The change in the position of a figure that moves it up, down, or sideways.
Example:

solid figure A figure that has length, width, and height.

sphere A solid figure in the shape of a ball.

square A quadrilateral with four right angles and all sides the same length.

square unit A square with sides 1 unit long, used to measure area.

standard form A way to write a number showing only its digits.
Example: 3,845

sum The answer to an addition problem.

survey Collect information by asking a number of people the same question and recording their answers.

symmetry A figure has symmetry if it can be folded along a line so that both parts match exactly.

tally chart A chart on which data is recorded.

tally mark A mark used to record data on a tally chart.
Example: 𝍤 = 5

tenth One of 10 equal parts of a whole, written as 0.1 or $\frac{1}{10}$.

thermometer A tool used to measure temperature.

third One of 3 equal parts of a whole.

trapezoid A quadrilateral with only one pair of parallel sides.

triangle A polygon with 3 sides.

turn (rotation) The change in the position of a figure that moves it around a point.
Example:

twelfth One of 12 equal parts of a whole.

twice Two times a number.

unit fraction A fraction with a numerator of 1.
Example: $\frac{1}{2}$

unlikely event An event that probably won't happen.

vertex (plural, vertices) The point where two rays meet to form an angle. The points where the sides of a polygon meet. The points where 3 or more edges meet in a solid figure that does not roll. The pointed part of a cone.

volume The number of cubic units needed to fill a solid figure.

week A unit of time equal to 7 days.

word form A number written in words.
Example: 9,325 = nine thousand, three hundred twenty-five

Y

yard (yd) A customary unit of length. 1 yard equals 3 feet or 36 inches.

Z

Zero Property of Multiplication The product of any number and zero is zero.

Illinois Performance Descriptors

	Page Numbers

Standard 6A Students who meet the standard can demonstrate knowledge and use of numbers and their many representations in a broad range of theoretical and practical settings.

6A.Stage C.1. Represent, order, and compare whole numbers to demonstrate an understanding of the base-ten number system.	**SE/TE: 12–13, 16–17, 34–35, 36–38, 40–42, 44–46, 50–52, 68–70, 72–73, 74–76, 78–79, 86–87, 88–89, 90–91, 92–94, 96–97, 98–100, 420–421, 422–424** 412–413, 416–417, 418–419, 426–428
6A.Stage C.2. Recognize equivalent representations of whole numbers and generate them by composing and decomposing numbers (e.g., 123 = 100 + 20 + 3).	**SE/TE: 4–5, 6–7, 8–9, 10–11, 32–33, 36–38, 50–52, 58–59, 86–87, 88–89, 90–91, 92–94, 96–97, 98–100, 108–109, 110–112**
6A.Stage C.3. Judge the size of fractions using models, benchmarks, and equivalent forms.	**SE/TE: 282–283, 316–318** 306–307, 308–311
6A.Stage C.4. Represent, order, label, and compare familiar fractions. Recognize and generate equivalent forms of familiar fractions.	**SE/TE: 284–286, 288–289, 306–307, 316–318** 308–311, 392–394
6A.Stage C.5. Explore and discuss uses of decimals.	**SE/TE: 308–311, 312–314** 306–307

Standard 6B Students who meet the standard can investigate, represent and solve problems using number facts, operations, and their properties, algorithms, and relationships.

6B.Stage C.1. Show and use the relationship between multiplication and division.	**SE/TE: 184–185**
6B.Stage C.2. Demonstrate and describe the effects of multiplying and dividing whole numbers using appropriate mathematical notation and vocabulary.	**SE/TE: 108–109, 110–112, 114–115, 116–117, 132–133, 164–165, 166–168, 170–171, 174–176, 184–185, 414–415, 416–417, 418–419, 420–421, 422–424, 426–428, 436–437, 438–439, 440–443, 444–445, 446–447, 448–450** 412–413
6B.Stage C.3. Explore, identify, and use relationships between and among properties of operations (e.g., commutativity applies to addition but not to subtraction).	**SE/TE: 32–33, 110–112** 122–124, 130–131
6B.Stage C.4. Demonstrate fluency with basic multiplication and division facts.	**SE/TE: 140–141, 142–143, 144–146, 148–149, 150–151, 152–153, 186–188, 190–191, 192–193, 194–195, 412–413, 414–415, 416–417, 418–419, 420–421, 422–424, 426–428, 436–437, 438–439, 444–445, 446–447, 448–450** 108–109, 110–112, 114–115, 116–117, 132–133
6B.Stage C.5. Solve multiplication and division number sentences and word problems.	**SE/TE: 108–109, 110–112, 114–115, 116–117, 118–120, 122–124, 126–127, 128–129, 130–131, 132–133, 172–173, 196–198, 412–413, 414–415, 416–417, 418–419, 420–421, 422–424, 426–428, 436–437, 438–439, 440–443, 444–445, 446–447, 448–450**

Bold indicates emphasis.

Illinois Performance Descriptors

	Page Numbers
6B.Stage C.6. Apply knowledge of basic multiplication facts (factors 0–10) to related facts (e.g., $3 \times 4 = 12$, $30 \times 4 = 120$, $300 \times 4 = 1200$).	**SE/TE: 412–413, 414–415, 416–417, 418–419, 420–421, 422–424** 426–428
6B.Stage C.7. Select and use one of various algorithms to add and subtract.	**SE/TE: 34–35, 36–38, 44–46, 48–49, 50–52, 54–55, 56–57, 58–59, 66–67, 68–70, 72–73, 74–76, 78–79, 86–87, 88–89, 90–91, 92–94, 96–97, 98–100, 312–314**

Standard 6C Students who meet the standard can compute and estimate using mental mathematics, paper-and-pencil methods, calculators, and computers.

6C.Stage C.1. Develop and use strategies (i.e. rounding) to estimate the results of whole-number computations and to judge the reasonableness of such results.	**SE/TE: 44–46, 48–49, 54–55, 56–57, 58–59, 74–76, 78–79, 88–89, 92–94, 98–100, 414–415, 426–428, 438–439**
6C.Stage C.2. Select appropriate methods and tools for computing with whole numbers from mental computation, estimation, calculators, and paper/pencil according to the context and nature of the computation and use of the selected method or tool.	**SE/TE: 34–35, 36–38, 44–46, 48–49, 50–52, 54–55, 56–57, 66–67, 68–70, 72–73, 74–76, 78–79, 86–87, 88–89, 90–91, 92–94, 96–97, 98–100, 108–109, 110–112, 114–115, 116–117, 132–133, 412–413, 414–415, 416–417, 418–419, 420–421, 422–424, 426–428, 436–437, 438–439, 440–443, 444–445, 446–447**
6C.Stage C.3. Determine whether exact answers or estimates are appropriate for solutions to problems.	**SE/TE: 74–76, 414B, 438–439** 414–415, 426–428

Standard 6D Students who meet the standard can solve problems using comparison of quantities, ratios, proportions, and percents.

6D.Stage C.1. Describe the relationship between two sets using ">", "<", and "=", "not equal to".	**SE/TE: 12–13, 34–35** 122–124, 130–131

Standard 7A Students who meet the standard can measure and compare quantities using appropriate units, instruments, and methods.

7A.Stage C.1. Explain the need for using standard units for measuring.	**SE/TE: 328–331, 332–333**
7A.Stage C.2. Measure objects using standard units in the U.S. customary and metric systems.	**SE/TE: 328–331, 332–333, 350–351**
7A.Stage C.3. Perform simple unit conversions within a system of measurement (e.g., three feet is the same as a yard).	**SE/TE: 334–337, 352–354, 398–399**
7A.Stage C.4. Describe multiple measurable attributes (e.g., length, mass/weight, time, temperature, area, volume, capacity) of a single object.	**SE/TE: 334–337, 338–339, 340–341**
7A.Stage C.5. Show and explain perimeter of an object by measuring and adding its linear units.	**SE/TE: 368–369, 370–371**
7A.Stage C.6. Show and explain the area of an object by counting square units.	**SE/TE: 376–377**

Bold indicates emphasis.

Illinois Performance Descriptors

	Page Numbers

Standard 7B Students who meet the standard can estimate measurements and determine acceptable levels of accuracy.

7B.Stage C.1. Develop and use common referents for linear measures to make comparisons and estimates.	**SE/TE: 328–331, 332–333, 334–337, 350–351, 352–354**
7B.Stage C.2. Estimate perimeter of simple polygons.	**SE/TE: 368–369, 370–371**

Standard 7C Students who meet the standard can select and use appropriate technology, instruments, and formulas to solve problems, interpret results, and communicate findings.

7C.Stage C.1. Select and apply appropriate standard units and tools to measure length, area, volume, weight, time, and temperature.	**SE/TE: 328–331, 332–333, 334–337, 338–339, 340–341, 356–357, 358–359, 392–394, 396–397, 398–399, 402–403, 404–405**
7C.Stage C.2. Determine elapsed time between events.	**SE/TE: 400–401, 404–405**
7C.Stage C.3. Solve problems using perimeter and area of simple polygons.	**SE/TE: 384–385**
7C.Stage C.4. Make change from a given amount using bills and coins.	**SE/TE: 22–23**

Standard 8A Students who meet the standard can describe numerical relationships using variables and patterns.

8A.Stage C.1. Extend geometric and simple numeric patterns using concrete objects or paper and pencil.	**SE/TE: 118–120, 206–207, 208–209, 218–221** 122–124, 126–127, 128–129, 130–131
8A.Stage C.2. Demonstrate how to create a pattern given a set of directions.	**SE/TE: 206B, 208–209** 206–207, 210–211
8A.Stage C.3. Identify errors in a given pattern.	**SE/TE: 212**
8A.Stage C.4. Represent the idea of a variable as an unknown quantity using a letter or a symbol in a numerical sentence.	**SE/TE: 68–70, 98–100, 132–133, 316–318** 108–109, 110–112
8A.Stage C.5. Express mathematical relationships using equations.	**SE/TE: 98–100, 108–109, 110–112, 150–151, 216–217, 222–223, 224–226, 316–318, 374–375, 398–399** 56–57, 58–59, 116–117, 132–133

Standard 8B Students who meet the standard can interpret and describe numerical relationships using tables, graphs, and symbols.

8B.Stage C.1. Represent and analyze simple patterns and operations using words, tables, and graphs.	**SE/TE: 118–120, 122–124, 126–127, 128–129, 130–131, 210–211, 298–299, 360–361**
8B.Stage C.2. Describe situations with constant rates of change using words, tables, and graphs (e.g., walking at a constant rate of speed).	**SE/TE: 118–120, 210–211, 212–214, 360–361**

Bold indicates emphasis.

Illinois Performance Descriptors

	Page Numbers
Standard 8C Students who meet the standard can solve problems using systems of numbers and their properties.	
8C.Stage C.1. Apply the relationship of multiplication and division fact families to solve for an unknown quantity.	**SE/TE: 184–185, 186–188**
Standard 8D Students who meet the standard can use algebraic concepts and procedures to represent and solve problems.	
8D.Stage C.1. Demonstrate how to select and use an appropriate operation to solve problems involving patterns (e.g., save one penny on day 1, double that amount each day for 10 days).	**SE/TE: 116–117, 118–120, 132–133, 360–361**
8D.Stage C.2. Solve one-step linear equations using concrete materials.	**SE/TE: 328–331, 332–333**
Standard 9A Students who meet the standard can demonstrate and apply geometric concepts involving points, lines, planes, and space.	
9A.Stage C.1. Specify locations using a coordinate system.	**SE/TE: 468–471**
9A.Stage C.2. Predict and describe the results of translations, rotations, and reflections of two-dimensional shapes.	**SE/TE: 260–262, 264–265, 266–267, 268–269**
9A.Stage C.3. Identify, draw, and build polygons.	**SE/TE: 246–247, 248–249, 250–251, 260–262, 264–265, 266–267, 268–269**
Standard 9B Students who meet the standard can identify, describe, classify and compare relationships using points, lines, planes, and solids.	
9B.Stage C.1. Decompose a three-dimensional object into two-dimensional components.	**SE/TE: 234–237, 238–240, 342–343**
9B.Stage C.2. Describe the difference between congruence and similarity.	**SE/TE: 260–262, 264–265**
9B.Stage C.3. Describe a motion or a series of motions that will show that two shapes are congruent.	**SE/TE: 260–262**
9B.Stage C.4. Identify and build a three-dimensional object from two-dimensional representations of that object.	**SE/TE: 241**
9B.Stage C.5. Apply geometric ideas and relationships to problems that arise in the classroom or in everyday life.	**SE/TE: 234–237, 238–240, 242–243, 244–245, 246–247, 248–249** 260–262, 264–265, 266–267, 268–269
9B.Stage C.6. Apply geometric ideas and relationships to other disciplines.	**SE/TE: 472–475**

Bold indicates emphasis.

Illinois Performance Descriptors

	Page Numbers
Standard 9C Students who meet the standard can construct convincing arguments and proofs to solve problems.	
9C.Stage C.1. Make and test conjectures about mathematical properties and relationships and justify the conclusions.	**SE/TE: 252–253** 260–262, 264–265
Standard 10A Students who meet the standard can organize, describe and make predictions from existing data.	
10A.Stage C.1. Organize, describe, and make predictions from existing data.	**SE/TE: 24–25, 458–459, 482–483**
10A.Stage C.2. Represent data using tables and graphs such as tallies and bar graphs.	**SE/TE: 458–459, 464–465, 466–467**
10A.Stage C.3. Describe the important features of a set of data displayed by a graph.	**SE/TE: 460–462**
10A.Stage C.4. Determine the median of data on a graph.	**SE/TE: 476–477**
Standard 10B Students who meet the standard can formulate questions, design data collection methods, gather and analyze data and communicate findings.	
10B.Stage C.1. Create and administer a survey considering which questions will be asked and how the answers will be recorded.	**SE/TE: 458–459**
10B.Stage C.2. Propose a follow-up survey to investigate questions that arise from the initial survey.	**TE: 458**
Standard 10C Students who meet the standard can determine, describe and apply the probabilities of events.	
10C.Stage C.1. Describe events as likely or unlikely and discuss the degree of likelihood using such words as certain, equally likely, and impossible.	**SE/TE: 472–475**
10C.Stage C.2. Explain probability as a fractional part of a group to the whole group (e.g., A tossed coin can land on heads or tails; therefore, it should land on heads $\frac{1}{2}$ of the time.).	**TE: 476**
10C.Stage C.3. Make predictions based on the results received from a probability experiment.	**SE/TE: 476–477**
10C.Stage C.4. Create and perform a probability experiment (e.g., a penny is flipped 100 times) and record the results.	**SE/TE: 476–477**
10C.Stage C.5. Understand that the measure of the likelihood of an event can be represented by a number from zero to one, inclusive.	**SE/TE: 472–475**

Bold indicates emphasis.

Illinois Assessment Framework Objectives

	Page Numbers
6.3.01 Read, write, recognize, and model equivalent representations of whole numbers and their place values up to 100,000.	SE/TE: 4–5, 6–7, 8–9, 10–11, 12–13, 16–17, 24–25, 50–52, 440–443
6.3.02 Identify and write (in words and standard form) whole numbers up to 100,000.	SE/TE: 4–5, 6–7, 8–9, 10–11
6.3.03 Recognize a fraction represented with a pictorial model.	SE/TE: 278–279, 280–281, 282–283, 306–307
6.3.04 Represent multiplication as repeated addition.	SE/TE: 108–109, 110–112
6.3.05 Order and compare whole numbers up to 10,000 using symbols (>, <, or =) and words (e.g., greater (more) than, less than, equal to, between).	SE/TE: 12–13, 16–17
6.3.06 Order and compare decimals expressed using monetary units.	SE/TE: 308–311
6.3.07 Identify and locate whole numbers and halves on a number line.	SE/TE: 32–33, 40–42, 290–293
6.3.08 Solve problems involving descriptions of numbers, including characteristics and relationships (e.g., odd/even, factors/multiples, greater than, less than).	SE/TE: 40–42, 108–109, 114–115, 116–117, 122–124, 126–127, 128–129, 130–131, 140–141, 142–143, 144–146, 148–149, 150–151, 152–153, 154–156, 166–168, 222–223, 224–226
6.3.09 Solve problems and number sentences involving addition and subtraction with regrouping.	SE/TE: 34–35, 36–38, 48–49, 50–52, 54–55, 56–57, 58–59, 68–70, 72–73, 86–87, 88–89, 90–91, 92–94, 96–97, 98–100
6.3.10 Solve problems involving the value of a collection of bills and coins whose total value is $10.00 or less, and make change.	SE/TE: 18–21, 22–23
6.3.11 Model and apply basic multiplication facts (up to 10 × 10), and apply them to related multiples of 10 (e.g., 3 × 4 = 12, 30 × 4 = 120).	SE/TE: 110–112, 114–115, 116–117, 118–120, 122–124, 126–127, 128–129, 130–131, 140–141, 142–143, 144–146, 148–149, 152–153, 412–413, 414–415, 416–417, 418–419, 420–421, 422–424
6.3.12 Use the inverse relationships between addition and subtraction to complete basic fact sentences and solve problems (e.g., 5 + 3 = 8 and 8 – 3 = __).	SE/TE: 66–67
6.3.13 Solve problems involving the multiplicative identity of one (e.g., 3 × 1 = 3) and the additive identity of zero (e.g., 3 + 0 = 3).	SE/TE: 130–131, 194–195
6.3.14 Make estimates appropriate to a given situation with whole numbers.	SE/TE: 44–46, 48–49, 54–55, 74–76, 92–94, 414–415, 438–439

Bold indicates emphasis.

Illinois Assessment Framework Objectives

	Page Numbers
7.3.01 Solve problems involving simple elapsed time in compound units (e.g., hours, minutes, days).	**SE/TE: 400–401**
7.3.02 Select and use appropriate standard units and tools to measure length (to the nearest inch or cm), time (to the nearest minute), and temperature (to the nearest degree).	**SE/TE: 328–331, 332–333, 350–351, 392–394, 396–397, 402–403, 404–405**
7.3.03 Solve problems involving the perimeter of a polygon with given side lengths or a given non-standard unit (e.g., paper clip).	**SE/TE: 368–369, 370–371, 372–373**
7.3.04 Solve problems involving the area of a figure when whole and half square units are shown within the figure.	**SE/TE: 376–377, 378–379, 384–385**
7.3.05 Compare and estimate length (including perimeter), area, and weight/mass using referents.	**SE/TE: 328–331, 340–341, 350–351, 358–359, 378–379**
7.3.06 Determine the volume of a solid figure that shows cubic units.	**SE/TE: 381–382**
7.3.07 Solve problems involving simple unit conversions <u>within the same measurement system</u> for time and length.	**SE/TE: 334–337, 352–354, 398–399**
8.3.01 Determine a missing term in a pattern (sequence), describe a pattern (sequence), and extend a pattern (sequence) when given a description or pattern (sequence).	**SE/TE: 206–207, 208–209, 210–211, 212–214, 218–221, 298–299, 360–361**
8.3.02 Write an expression to represent a given situation.	**SE/TE: 216–217, 224–226**
8.3.03 Represent simple mathematical relationships with number sentences (equations and inequalities).	**SE/TE: 66–67, 98–100, 118–120, 154–156, 196–198, 222–223, 316–318, 426–428, 448–450**
8.3.04 Solve one-step addition and subtraction equations that have a missing number or missing operation sign (e.g., $3 + \square = 5$, $6 \square 1 = 7$).	**SE/TE: 32–33, 36–38, 66–67, 72–73**
8.3.05 Solve word problems involving unknown quantities.	**SE/TE: 58–59, 66–67, 78–79, 98–100, 132–133, 154–156, 174–176, 196–198, 224–226, 298–299, 320–321, 374–375, 384–385, 404–405, 426–428, 448–450**
9.3.01 Identify, describe, and sketch two-dimensional shapes (triangles, squares, rectangles, pentagons, hexagons, and octagons) according to the number of sides, length of sides, and number of vertices.	**SE/TE: 246–247, 248–249, 250–251, 252–253**

Bold indicates emphasis.

Illinois Assessment Framework Objectives

	Page Numbers
9.3.02 Identify and describe three-dimensional shapes (cubes, spheres, cones, cylinders, prisms, and pyramids) according to their characteristics (faces, edges, vertices).	**SE/TE: 234–237, 238–240, 342–343**
9.3.03 Locate and identify points using numbers and symbols on a grid, and describe how points relate to each other on a grid (e.g., solid heart shape is 2 units below sun symbol, point A is 3 units to the right of point B).	**SE/TE: 468–471**
9.3.04 Identify whether or not a figure has a line of symmetry, and sketch or identify the line of symmetry.	**SE/TE: 264–265, 266–267**
9.3.05 Identify images resulting from flips (reflections), slides (translations), or turns (rotations).	**SE/TE: 260–262**
9.3.06 Identify parallel lines.	**SE/TE: 242–243**
9.3.07 Identify the two-dimensional components of a three-dimensional object (e.g., a cube has square faces).	**SE/TE: 238–240**
9.3.08 Identify a three-dimensional object from its net.	**SE/TE: 241**
9.3.09 Predict the result of putting shapes together (composing) and taking them apart (decomposing).	**SE/TE: 268–269**
9.3.10 Identify congruent and similar figures by visual inspection.	**SE/TE: 260–262**
9.3.11 Determine the distance between two points on the number line in whole numbers.	**SE/TE: 32–33, 40–42**
10.3.01 Read and interpret data represented in a pictograph, bar graph, Venn diagram (with two circles), tally chart, or table.	**SE/TE: 458–459, 460–462, 482–483**
10.3.02 Complete missing parts of a pictograph, bar graph, tally chart, or table for a given set of data.	**SE/TE: 464–465, 466–467**
10.3.03 Determine the mode, given a set of data or a graph.	**TE: 480**
10.3.04 Classify events using words such as certain, most likely, equally likely, least likely, possible, and impossible.	**SE/TE: 472–475, 476–477**
10.3.05 Describe the chances associated with a context presented visually, including using the response format "3 out of 4."	**TE: 478**

NCTM Curriculum Focal Points and Connections for Grade 3

The set of three curriculum focal points and related connections for mathematics in Grade 3 follow. These topics are the recommended content emphases for this grade level. It is essential that these focal points be addressed in contexts that promote problem solving, reasoning, communication, making connections, and designing and analyzing representations.

Grade 3 Curriculum Focal Points	Page Numbers
Number and Operations and **Algebra**: Developing understandings of multiplication and division and strategies for basic multiplication facts and related division facts	
Students understand the meanings of multiplication and division of whole numbers through the use of representations (e.g., equal-sized groups, arrays, area models, and equal "jumps" on number lines for multiplication, and successive subtraction, partitioning, and sharing for division).	108–109, 110–112, 114–115, 116–117, 118–120, 122–133, 140–157, 164–165, 166–168, 170–171, 172–176, 184–185, 186–193, 194–195, 196–199, 376–377, 412–429
They use properties of addition and multiplication (e.g., commutativity, associativity, and the distributive property) to multiply whole numbers and apply increasingly sophisticated strategies based on these properties to solve multiplication and division problems involving basic facts.	33, 95, 110, 131, 153, 175, 184–193, 194–195
By comparing a variety of solution strategies, students relate multiplication and division as inverse operations.	184–193
Number and Operations: Developing an understanding of fractions and fraction equivalence	
Students develop an understanding of the meanings and uses of fractions to represent parts of a whole, parts of a set, or points or distances on a number line.	276–277, 278–279, 280–281, 282–283, 290–293, 306–307
They understand that the size of a fractional part is relative to the size of the whole, and they use fractions to represent numbers that are equal to, less than, or greater than 1.	276–277, 278–279, 280–281, 282–283, 290–293
They solve problems that involve comparing and ordering fractions by using models, benchmark fractions, or common numerators or denominators.	282–283, 288–289, 290–293
They understand and use models, including the number line, to identify equivalent fractions.	284–287, 290–293
Geometry: Describing and analyzing properties of two-dimensional shapes	
Students describe, analyze, compare, and classify two-dimensional shapes by their sides and angles and connect these attributes to definitions of shapes.	244–245, 246–247, 248–249, 250–251, 252–253
Students investigate, describe, and reason about decomposing, combining, and transforming polygons to make other polygons.	241, 268–269
Through building, drawing, and analyzing two-dimensional shapes, students understand attributes and properties of two-dimensional space and the use of those attributes and properties in solving problems, including applications involving congruence and symmetry.	244–245, 260–263, 264–265, 266–267, 268–269

Connections to the Focal Points

	Page Numbers
Algebra	
Understanding properties of multiplication and the relationship between multiplication and division is a part of algebra readiness that develops at grade 3.	32–33, 95, 110, 131, 153, 184–185, 186–193, 425
The creation and analysis of patterns and relationships involving multiplication and division should occur at this grade level.	121–129, 184–193, 206–207, 208–209, 210–211, 212–214, 412–413
Students build a foundation for later understanding of functional relationships by describing relationships in context with such statements as, "The number of legs is 4 times the number of chairs."	114–115, 210–211, 212–214, 216–217
Measurement	
Students in grade 3 strengthen their understanding of fractions as they confront problems in linear measurement that call for more precision than the whole unit allowed them in their work in grade 2.	328–331, 332–333
They develop their facility in measuring with fractional parts of linear units.	332–333
Students develop measurement concepts and skills through experiences in analyzing attributes and properties of two-dimensional objects.	246–247, 248–249, 250–251, 252–253, 372–373
They form an understanding of perimeter as a measurable attribute and select appropriate units, strategies, and tools to solve problems involving perimeter.	368–369, 370–371, 372–373
Data Analysis	
Addition, subtraction, multiplication, and division of whole numbers come into play as students construct and analyze frequency tables, bar graphs, picture graphs, and line plots and use them to solve problems.	458–459, 460–462, 464–465, 466–467, 468–471, 472–475, 476–477, 478–481, 482–483
Number and Operations	
Building on their work in grade 2, students extend their understanding of place value to numbers up to 10,000 in various contexts.	4–5, 6–7, 8–9, 10–11, 12–15, 16–17, 18–21, 24–25
Students also apply this understanding to the task of representing numbers in different equivalent forms (e.g., expanded notation).	4–5, 6–7, 8–9, 10–11
They develop their understanding of numbers by building their facility with mental computation (addition and subtraction in special cases, such as 2,500 + 6,000 and 9,000 – 5,000), by using computational estimation, and by performing paper-and-pencil computations.	34–35, 36–39, 40–43, 44–46, 48–57, 68–71, 72–73, 74–76, 78–79, 86–101, 126–127, 150–151, 306–314, 412–424, 436–450

OBJECTIVES

NUMBER PROPERTIES AND OPERATIONS

1) Number sense

a) Identify the place value and actual value of digits in whole numbers.

b) Represent numbers using models such as base 10 representations, number lines, and two-dimensional models.

c) Compose or decompose whole quantities by place value (e.g., write whole numbers in expanded notation using place value: 342= 300 + 40 + 2).

d) Write or rename whole numbers (e.g., 10: 5 + 5, 12 - 2, 2 x 5).

e) Connect model, number word, or number using various models and representations for whole numbers, fractions, and decimals.

f) Order or compare whole numbers, decimals, or fractions.

2) Estimation

a) Use benchmarks (well known numbers used as meaningful points for comparison) for whole numbers, decimals, or fractions in contexts (e.g., 1/2 and .5 may be used as benchmarks for fractions and decimals between 0 and 1.00).

b) Make estimates appropriate to a given situation with whole numbers, fractions, or decimals by:
  • knowing when to estimate,
  • selecting the appropriate type of estimate, including overestimate, underestimate, and range of estimate, or
  • selecting the appropriate method of estimation (e.g., rounding).

c) Verify solutions or determine the reasonableness of results in meaningful contexts.

3) Number operations

a) Add and subtract:
  • whole numbers, or
  • fractions with like denominators, or decimals through hundredths.

b) Multiply whole numbers:
  • No larger than two-digit by two-digit with paper and pencil computation, or
  • larger numbers with use of calculator.

c) Divide whole numbers:
  • Up to three-digits by one-digit with paper and pencil computation, or
  • Up to five-digits by two-digits with use of calculator.

d) Describe the effect of operations on size (whole numbers).

e) Interpret whole numbers operations and the relationships between them.

f) Solve application problems involving numbers and operations.

4) Ratios and proportional reasoning

a) Use simple ratios to describe problem situations.

5) Properties of number and operations

a) Identify odd and even numbers.

b) Identify factors of whole numbers.

c) Apply basic properties of operations.

d) Explain or justify a mathematical concept or relationship (e.g., explain why 15 is an odd number or why 7–3 is not the same as 3–7).

MEASUREMENT

1) Measuring physical attributes

a) Identify the attribute that is appropriate to measure in a given situation.

b) Compare objects with respect to a given attribute, such as length, area, volume, time, or temperature.

c) Estimate the size of an object with respect to a given measurement attribute (e.g., length or perimeter).

d) Select or use appropriate measurement instruments such as rulers, meter sticks, clocks, thermometers, or other scaled instruments.

e) Solve problems involving perimeter of plane figures.

f) Solve problems involving area of rectangles.

2) Systems of measurement

a) Select or use appropriate type of unit for the attribute being measured, such as length, time, or temperature.

b) Solve problems involving conversions within the same measurement systems, such as conversions involving inches and feet or hours and minutes.

c) Determine appropriate size of units of measurement in problem situation involving such attributes as length, time, capacity, or weight.

d) Determine situations in which a highly accurate measurement is important.

GEOMETRY

1) Dimension and shape

a) Explore properties of paths between points.

b) Describe (informally) real world objects using simple plane figures (e.g., triangles, rectangles, squares and circles) and simple solid figures (e.g., cubes, spheres, and cylinders).

c) Identify or draw angles and other geometric figures in the plane.

d) Describe attributes of two- and three-dimensional shapes.

2) Transformation of shapes and preservation of properties

a) Identify whether a figure is symmetrical, or draw lines of symmetry.

b) Identify the images resulting from flips (reflections), slides (translations) or turns (rotations).

c) Recognize which attributes (such as shape and area) change or don't change when plane figures are cut up and rearranged.

d) Match or draw congruent figures in a given collection.

3) Relationships between geometric figures

a) Analyze or describe patterns of geometric figures by increasing number of sides, changing size or orientation (e.g., polygons with more and more sides).

b) Assemble simple plane shapes to construct a given shape.

c) Recognize two-dimensional faces of three-dimensional shapes.

4) Position and direction

a) Describe relative positions of points and lines using the geometric ideas of parallelism or perpendicularity.

b) Construct geometric figures with vertices at points on a coordinate grid.

5) Mathematical reasoning

a) Distinguish which objects in a collection satisfy a given geometric definition and explain choices.

DATA ANALYSIS AND PROBABILITY

1) Data representation

The following representations of data are indicated for each grade level. Objectives in which only a subset of these representations is applicable are indicated in the parentheses associated with the objective.

Pictograms, bar graphs, circle graphs, line graphs, line plots, tables, and tallies.

a) Read or interpret a single set of data.

b) Given a set of data, complete a graph (limits of time make it difficult to construct graphs completely).

c) Solve problems by estimating and computing within a single set of data.

2) Characteristics of data sets

a) Given a set of data or a graph, describe the distribution of the data using median, range, or mode.

b) Compare two sets of related data.

3) Experiments and samples

4) Probability

a) Use informal probabilistic thinking to describe chance events (i.e., likely and unlikely, certain and impossible).

b) List all possible outcomes of a given situation or event.

c) Represent the probability of a given outcome from pictures of spinners and other devices.

ALGEBRA

1) Patterns, relations, and functions

a) Recognize, describe, or extend numerical patterns.

b) Given a pattern or sequence, construct or explain a rule that can generate the terms of the pattern or sequence.

c) Given a description, extend or find a missing term in a pattern or sequence.

d) Create a different representation of a pattern or sequence given a verbal description.

e) Recognize or describe a relationship in which quantities change proportionally.

2) Algebraic representations

a) Translate between the different forms of representations (symbolic, numerical, verbal, or pictorial) of whole number relationships (such as from a written description to an equation or from a function table to a written description).

b) Graph or interpret points with whole number or letter coordinates on grids or in the first quadrant of the coordinate plane.

c) Verify a conclusion using algebraic properties.

3) Variables, expressions, and operations

a) Use letters and symbols to represent an unknown quantity in a simple mathematical expression.

b) Express simple mathematical relationships using number sentences.

4) Equations and inequalities

a) Find the value of the unknown in a whole number sentence.

Books in the MathStart® Series

Animals on Board (Adding)
Beep, Beep, Vroom Vroom! (Pattern Recognition)
The Best Bug Parade (Comparing Sizes)
The Best Vacation Ever (Collecting Data)
Betcha! (Estimating)
Bigger, Better, Best! (Area)
Bug Dance (Directions)
Captain Invincible and the Space Shapes (Three-dimensional shapes)
Circle Shapes (Recognizing Shapes)
Dave's Down to Earth Rock Shop (Classifying)
Dinosaur Deals (Equivalent Values)
Divide and Ride (Dividing)
Double the Ducks (Doubling Numbers)
Earth Day Hooray! (Place Value)
Elevator Magic (Subtracting)
Every Buddy Counts (Counting)
A Fair Bear Share (Regrouping)
Game Time! (Time)
Get Up and Go! (Timelines)
Give Me Half! (Understanding Halves)
The Greatest Gymnast of All (Opposites)
The Grizzly Gazette (Percentage)
Hamster Champs (Angles)
Henry the Fourth (Ordinals)
A House for Birdie (Understanding Capacity)
It's About Time (Hours)
Jack the Builder (Counting On)
Jump, Kangaroo, Jump! (Fractions)
Just Enough Carrots (Comparing Amounts)
Leaping Lizards (Counting by 5s and 10s)
Lemonade for Sale (Bar Graphs)

Less than Zero (Negative Numbers)
Let's Fly a Kite (Symmetry)
Mall Mania (Addition Strategies)
Mighty Maddie (Odd and Even Numbers)
Missing Mittens (Odd and Even Numbers)
Monster Musical Chairs (Subtracting One)
More or Less (Comparing Numbers)
One... Two... Three... Sassafras! (Number Order)
100 Days of Cool (Numbers 1–100)
A Pair of Socks (Matching)
The Penny Pot (Counting Coins)
Pepper's Journal (Calendars)
Polly's Pen Pal (Metrics)
Probably Pistachio (Probability)
Rabbit's Pajama Party (Sequencing)
Racing Around (Perimeter)
Ready, Set, Hop! (Building Equations)
Rodeo Time (Reading a Schedule)
Room for Ripley (Capacity)
Safari Park (Solving for Unknowns)
Same Old Horse (Making Predictions)
Seaweed Soup (Matching Sets)
Shark Swimathon (Subtracting 2-Digit Numbers)
Sluggers' Car Wash (Dollars and Cents)
The Sundae Soup (Combinations)
Super Sand Castle Saturday (Measuring)
Spunky Monkeys on Parade (Counting by 2s, 3s, and 4s)
Tally O'Malley (Tallying)
3 Little Firefighters (Sorting)
Too Many Kangaroo Things to Do! (Multiplication)
Treasure Map (Mapping)

T

U

V

W

Y

Z

Scott Foresman-Addison Wesley
enVisionMATH.

Cover:
Luciana Powell

Illustrations:
Dick Gage 8, 12, 16, 38, 54, 146, 350; Leslie Kell 10, 11, 76, 88, 122, 123, 140, 143, 144, 166, 168, 237, 265, 267, 261, 281, 282, 283, 298, 301, 302, 345, 369, 386, 414, 422, 446, 448; Neil Stewart 55, 92, 124, 146, 174, 331, 336, 351, 352, 353, 360, 386; Joe LeMonnier 195, 279, 280

Photographs:
Every effort has been made to secure permission and provide appropriate credit for photographic material. The publisher deeply regrets any omission and pledges to correct errors called to its attention in subsequent editions.

Unless otherwise acknowledged, all photographs are the property of Scott Foresman, a division of Pearson Education.

Photo locators denoted as follows: Top (T), Center (C), Bottom (B), Left (L), Right (R), Background (Bkgd)

2 ©Roy Beusker/Weijers Domino Productions b.v.; 3 ©Will & Deni McIntyre/Getty Images; 6 ©Dave King/©DK Images; 14 (TR) Purestock/Alamy Images, (CR) ©Brad Perks Lightscapes/Alamy (BC) Getty Images (BC) Jupiter Images; 17 (CR) Jerry Young/©DK Images (R) ©WizData, Inc./Alamy (L) Dave King/©DK Images (CL) ©Kennan Ward/Corbis; 21 ©John Van Hasselt/Corbis; 28 Getty Images 30 (T) ©Ken Usami/Getty Images (B) ©Kristin Siebeneicher/AP Images (R) Westend61/Alamy Images (C) Getty Images; 35 ©Wyman Meinzer; 38 (CL) Getty Images (C) IT Stock Free/Jupiter Images; 42 (CR) Kathleen Murtagh (BR) Westend61/Alamy Images; 44 ©Royalty-Free/Corbis; 49 (BL) Getty Images (BL) ©photolibrary/Index Open (CL) Stockdisc (C) ©Photos Select/Index Open (BR) ©photolibrary/Index Open; 56 (CR) ©imagebroker/Alamy (C) Frank Greenaway/©DK Images (TR) ©imagebroker/Alamy; 57 ©John Luke/Index Open; 64 (T) Joe Tucciarone/Photo Researchers, Inc. (C) NASA Image Exchange (B) ©Christian Kober/Alamy Images (R) Getty Images (L) Frans Lanting Photography; 70 Getty Images; 73 ©David Wootton/Alamy Images; 84 (L) ©David R. Frazier Photolibrary, Inc./Alamy Images (T) Blickwinkel/fotototo/Alamy Images (B) Getty Images (C) ©Christian Kober/Alamy Images (R) ©Ron Watts/Corbis; 94 ©David R. Frazier Photolibrary, Inc./Alamy Images; 106 (T) ©Jill Stephenson/Alamy (B) Blickwinkel/fotototo/Alamy Images (C) ©Wyman Meinzer (R) Getty Images; 138 (L) NASA/JPL-Caltech/M. Kelley (Univ. of Minnesota)/NASA (TL) ©Geoff du Feu/Alamy (B) ©Les Chatfield (BL) Bettmann/Corbis (BC) ©Steven Puetzer/Getty Images; 162 (BL)

©Jim Cummins/Corbis (B) NASA (TR) Getty Images; 176 Getty Images; 182 (CR) ©Hulton Archive/Getty Images (B) ©Brad Rickerby/Getty Images (TL) Getty Images; 184 Getty Images; 198 (T) Archivberlin Fotoagentur GmbH/Alamy Images (B) Juniors Bildarchiv/Alamy Images; 204 (CL) KIKE CALVO / VWPICS/Alamy Images (B) ©Panoramic Images/Getty Images (L) Digital Vision 209 ©Directphoto/Alamy; 210 Jupiter Images; 214 ©Alissa Crandall/Corbis; 232 (TL) Desmond Boylan/Reuters Media (BL) ©Baron Wolman/Getty Images (B) Andy King/Orange Dot Productions; 233 ©Kim Karpeles/Alamy Images; 234 (BL) Jupiter Images (BR) ©photolibrary/Index Open; 235 (BL) ©Vstock/Index Open (BC) ©photolibrary/Index Open; 236 (C) Stockdisc (BC) Getty Images (BR) Getty Images; 243 ©Baron Wolman/Getty Images; 251 Andy King/Orange Dot Productions; 258 (TL) Desmond Boylan/Reuters Media (BL) ©Baron Wolman/Getty Images (BL) ©Alan Weintraub/Alamy Images (C) Andy King/Orange Dot Productions; 267 ©Photos Select/Index Open; 274 (TL) ©Lester V. Bergman/Corbis (B) Photowood Inc./Corbis (BL) Dream Maker Software (TC) WildPictures/Alamy Images (TL) Ed Reschke/Peter Arnold/Alamy Images; 283 ©Lester V. Bergman/Corbis; 293 (B) James Robinson/Animals Animals/Earth Scenes (TC) ©Stefan Sollfors Insects/Alamy (TR) ©Creatas; 304 (BL) ©Simon Belcher/Alamy (TL) Photo Researchers, Inc.; 308 ©Vstock/Index Open; 310 Getty Images; 326 (C) ©Simple Stock Shots (TL) Mary Evans Picture Library/Alamy Images (BL) Gary Roberts/Rex USA; 328 Mary Evans Picture Library/Alamy Images; 329 Jupiter Images; 332 (T) ©photolibrary/Index Open (CL) Corbis (BL) Getty Images; 333 (TR) Jupiter Images (CL) ©Photos Select/Index Open (CR) ©Photos Select/Index Open (B) ©Mistral Images/Index Open; 335 Getty Images; 338 (CR) ©Image Source Limited (BL) ©Comstock Inc. (BC) G. Huntington (BR) Jupiter Images; 339 ©Simple Stock Shots; 340 (TR) ©Royalty-Free/Corbis (BL) Getty Images (BR) ©S. Hurst/Alamy (CL) Getty Images (C) BAN/©Pearson (L) Jupiter Images (R) Getty Images; 341 Associated Press/AP Images; 344 (BC) Getty Images (BR) Corbis (TCR) ©Vstock/Index Open; 345 (TL) Getty Images (CR) Corbis; 346 (TR) Stockdisc Stockdisc (BR) ©Royalty-Free/Corbis (CR) ©Photos Select/Index Open (CL) Jupiter Images; 348 (TR) Ingrid van den Berg/AGE Fotostock (TL) Getty Images (BL) ©Wolfgang Pilzer/Alamy Images (B) Digital Vision; 350 (T) ©Creatas (CL) Digital Vision (BL) Herrera Technologies (B) Foodcollection/Getty Images (TL) ©photolibrary/Index Open; 351 (CL) ©Jim Lane/Alamy Images (CR) ©Michele Westmorland/Corbis (R)

Jupiter Images (BL) (CL) Getty Images (TR) ©Creatas; 354 PCL/Alamy Images; 356 (CL) ©photolibrary/Index Open (BL) Karen Mancinelli/©Pearson (BC) Pearson Learning/©Pearson (BR) ©Simple Stock Shots; 357 (BR) Juergen & Christine Sohns/Animals Animals/Earth Scenes (BC) Simple Stock Shots; 358 (CR) Stockdisc (BL) Jupiter Images (BC) Getty Images; 364 (CR) MIXA/Getty Images (BR) Pearson Learning/©Pearson; 365 (TL) Getty Images (C) ©photolibrary/Index Open; 366 (CL) Jeff Saward/Labyrinthos Picture Library (TR) Jeff Saward/Labyrinthos Picture Library; 371 W. Blaine Pennington Photo; 390 (B) ©David Maitland/Getty Images (CL) ©Bill Varie/Corbis (B) Thinkstock/Jupiter Images (L) NASA Image Exchange (TR) ©Jeff Rotman (Avi Klapfer)/Nature Picture Library; 391 ©Adam Woolfitt/Corbis; 398 Getty Images; 403 (T) Getty Images (TR) Getty Images (BR) John Paul Endress/©Pearson (B) Jupiter Images; 410 (BL) ©Stephen Street/Alamy Images (BR) ©Douglas Faulkner/Alamy Images (TL) ©Mike Hill/Alamy Images(B) ©Miodrag Nejkovic/Alamy Images (TC) NASA Image Exchange; 424 Alain Dragesco-Joffe/Animals Animals/Earth Scenes; 434 (TL) ©Tim Shaffer/Corbis (TCL) Getty Images (TL) ©Paul Sakuma/AP Images (TR) ©Joe McBride/Getty Images (T) ©Hot Ideas/Index Open (C) DK Images (TL) Roger Harris/Photo Researchers, Inc.; 456 (L) ©Eric Hosking/Corbis (C) Ingram Publishing/Jupiter Images (BL) ©Adam Pretty/Getty Images; 472 ©Kerem Su/China Span/Alamy Images.

Student Edition

Photographs

Every effort has been made to secure permission and provide appropriate credit for photographic material. The publisher deeply regrets any omission and pledges to correct errors called to its attention in subsequent editions.

Unless otherwise acknowledged, all photographs are the property of Scott Foresman, a division of Pearson Education.

Photo locators denoted as follows: Top (T), Center (C), Bottom (B), Left (L), Right (R), Background (Bkgd)

Scott Foresman • Addison Wesley